# COMPLEMENTARY APPROACHES FOR USING ECOTOXICITY DATA IN SOIL POLLUTION EVALUATION

# COMPLEMENTARY APPROACHES FOR USING ECOTOXICITY DATA IN SOIL POLLUTION EVALUATION

## M. D. FERNANDEZ AND J. V. TARAZONA

Nova Science Publishers, Inc.
*New York*

LIBRARY OF CONGRESS CATALOGING-IN-PUBLICATION DATA
Fernandez, M. D.
  Complementary approaches for using ecotoxicity data in soil pollution evaluation / M.D. Fernandez, J.V. Tarazona.
    p. cm.
  ISBN 978-1-60692-105-0 (softcover)
  1. Soil pollution. I. Tarazona, Jose V., 1959- II. Title.
  TD878.F47 2008
  628.5'5--dc22
                    2008033150

*Published by Nova Science Publishers, Inc.* ✦*New York*

# CONTENTS

# PREFACE

The assessment of soil quality has usually focused on human health protection as the main objective. Recently, criteria for the protection of ecosystems have been incorporated and ecotoxicological analyses are recommended to estimate the risk to ecological receptors associated with contaminants in soils (Calow, 1993; Stephenson et al., 2002; Loibner et al., 2003; Robidoux et al., 2004b). The ecotoxicological assessment of soils is mostly based on the toxicity test with selected organisms. Two complementary approaches are available. The first approach consists in the identification of toxicity thresholds for each relevant pollutant, thresholds that are based on the evaluation of effects of chemical substances on selected organisms representing relevant ecological receptors. The results of these assays are used for setting soil quality standards for each pollutant or pollutant class. Risk assessment tools can be used for this purpose, pre-establishing acceptable levels of risk. The contamination level is based on the comparison of the concentration of contaminants measured in the soil with the standards established from the thresholds. Although field and semi-field information can be incorporated in the higher tier steps, the thresholds are mostly developed from standardised toxicity assays conducted under laboratory conditions following international (e.g. OECD, ISO) or national (e.g. USEPA, ASTM) guidelines. In the second approach, toxicity assays are performed directly with the contaminated media (soil, water, sediment). This alternative, performing the assays with environmental samples, constitutes the method called direct (eco)toxicity assessment (DTA), and is based on modified bioassays.

Most regulations have developed soil quality standards based on toxicity assays. However, due to the limitations in the lab to field extrapolation, trends were directed towards the combination of chemical analysis and DTA (Peterson et al., 1990; Torstensson, 1993; Tørsløv et al., 1997). In this chapter, both alternatives will be compared. The main difference between both approaches is that in the first case, a reference "uncontaminated" soil sample is spiked with one or a few chemicals at different concentrations, while in the DTA approach real soil samples are collected at the contaminated site, therefore containing a realistic combination of the different pollutants present in the area, the field sample can be then tested and/or "diluted" with "uncontaminated" soil to create a pollution gradient. The toxicity of the spiked or collected/diluted samples is measured and concentration/response relationships obtained in both cases. To understand better this comparison, in this chapter the term "toxicity test" will be used for the first approach: toxicity tests with samples spiked at the lab; while the term "bioassay" will be used for the DTA approach: samples collected at the field.

*Chapter 1*

# TOXICITY TEST FOR THE ASSESSMENT
# OF CONTAMINATED SOILS

Toxicity testing consists in the evaluation of the degree to which an individual substance or a mixture of substances adversely affects living organisms. Tests may be performed at different levels of biological organisation, from molecular level (biochemical changes) to ecosystem. Reproducibility increases from molecular to ecosystem level, whereas the relevance increases in the opposite direction. Therefore, compromise decisions in terms of sensitivity, ecological relevance and predictive potential must be taken and consequently, most protocols are performed at the organism level, constituting the "single-species toxicity tests".

During the test, key test organisms are exposed to toxic agents and the response is observed during and/or at the end of the test. Different endpoints are used to measure the toxic effect. These endpoints are related to a measurable characteristic of the test organism, which can be affected by toxicants. They may be lethal responses (mortality) or sublethal effects (e.g. inhibition of growth or reproduction). The response is also associated to the exposure time; adverse effects may occur after short or long-term exposures. Times should be related to the lifetime of the test organisms. Short-terms exposures are useful to observe acute effects; while extended periods covering a significant part of the life cycle are required to address chronic effects. Taking into account that a pollution situation mostly involves long term exposures to low concentrations, the chronic assessment usually represents more realistic situations.

In toxicology, it is fundamental to establish the relation between the amount of chemical to which an organism is exposed and the magnitude of the response. Thus, a common method for measuring toxicity is to expose the organisms to a concentration gradient. The results may be expressed in two ways: the concentration which will cause a toxic response at a determined level or the highest concentration which will not cause an effect. In the first case toxicity may be expressed as median lethal concentration (LC50) or median effect concentration (EC50), which represents the concentration that produces/causes mortality or the measured effect in 50% of the test organisms, respectively. Other effect levels such as L(E)C10 are also used. The effects can be represented by levels that estimate the concentration at which a specified percentage of impairment occurs. The term IC50 is sometimes employed, instead of the EC50, to express the concentration that inhibits/reduces the response observed in the control by a 50%. In this case, the measure is not a quantal but a quantitative one. For example, in the algae growth inhibition test, the measure is expressed as IC value because it focuses in changes in the growth and not in the number of organisms that show effect. These parameters are usually used in acute assays. Values are estimated by a linear regression performing a transformation of response data, for instance using a logit-probit (Litchfield and Wilcoxon, 1949) or Weibull units (Christensen and Nyholm, 1984). The highest concentration which causes no toxicity is usually expressed as No Observed Effect Concentration (NOEC) and it is used in chronic assays. In addition, LOEC is defined as the lowest concentration at which effects are observed. These endpoints are based on statistical techniques; the effects determined for a particular concentration are compared with the control response using analysis of variance (ANOVA). The soil means must be compared using an appropriate multiple comparison test method. Dunnett´s method is perhaps the most widely used method in ecotoxicology. These methods take account of the multiple statistical tests by adjusting the statistical threshold for declaring significance. The NOEC represents the highest tested concentration at which no statistically significant differences with the control are observed.

The toxicity assays used in soil characterization protocols can be grouped, according to their complexity, in: laboratory assays with single species, multispecies tests and soil microcosms. Larger systems, equivalent to the aquatic mesocosms, and (semi)field assays are often used to assess fate properties but they are scarcely employed for the effect assessment. Assays have been developed to evaluate impacts of chemicals on the diverse communities of microorganisms, plants and invertebrate and vertebrate animals that comprise the terrestrial ecosystem (Stephenson et al., 2002; Loibner et al., 2003). Many single species assays have been standardized to harmonize their use with the aim of reducing variability and comparing results. In contrast to aquatic toxicity, testing protocols for soils are less developed. However, as already mentioned, notable efforts are being made by different organizations (ISO; OCDE; USEPA, ASTM, etc) to standardize soil toxicity assays. These assays can be used to test lab spiked or field contaminated soils and may also be used to monitor remediation processes. In table 1 the tests to soil and aquatic organisms standardized by OCDE are shown. These tests have been widely used to aid the process of risk assessment.

**Table 1. OCDE standardized tests for the determination of the toxicity of chemical substances to soil and aquatic organisms**

| Taxonomic group | Title | Endpoint | Measurement variables | Assay time (days) | Test Number |
|---|---|---|---|---|---|
| Terrestrial invertebrates | Earthworm, acute toxicity test | Survival | Number of living worms | 14 | 207 |
| Terrestrial invertebrates | Enchytraeid, reproduction test | Reproduction | Number of juvenile worms | 42 | 220 |
| Terrestrial invertebrates | Earthworm reproduction test | Reproduction | Number of living offspring and cocoon numbers | 56 | 222 |
| Plants | Terrestrial plant test: seedling emergence and seedling growth test | Emergence of seedlings and Inhibition of growth | Emergence, dry shoot weight (fresh weight), shoot weight and assessment of visible detrimental effects | 14-21 | 208 |
| Plants | Terrestrial plants test: vegetative vigor test | Vegetative vigor and growth | Biomass (dry shoot weight) and visible detrimental effects | 21-28 | 227 |
| Microorganisms | Soil microorganisms: Nitrogen transformation tests | Nitrogen transformation | Rate of nitrate production | 28 | 216 |
| Microorganisms | Soil microorganisms: Carbon transformation tests | Carbon transformation | Glucose-induced respiration rates | 28 | 217 |
| Algae Cyanobacteria | Freshwater Alga and Cyanobacteria, Growth inhibition test | Inhibition of growth | Algal biomass: cell counts, cell volume, fluorescence, optical density, etc. | 4 | 201 |
| Aquatic Invertebrates | Daphnia s.p., Acute immobilization test | Survival | Immobilization | 1 | 202 |
| Aquatic Invertebrates | Daphnia magna, reproduction test | Reproduction | Number of living offspring | 21 | 211 |
| Fish | Fish, Acute toxicity test | Survival | Number of living fish | 4 | 203 |
| Fish | Fish, Prolonged toxicity test: 14-day study | Survival, appearance and behavior, and growth | Survival, abnormalities (appearance and behavior), length and weight | 14 | 204 |

## Table 1. (Continued)

| Taxonomic group | Title | Endpoint | Measurement variables | Assay time (days) | Test Number |
|---|---|---|---|---|---|
| Fish | Fish, early-life stage toxicity test | Survival, appearance and behavior, and growth | Hatching and survival (at different stages), abnormalities (appearance and behavior), length and weight | 30-60 | 210 |
| Fish | Fish, short-term toxicity test on embryo and sac-fry stages | Survival, appearance and behavior, and growth | Hatching and survival (at different stages), abnormalities (appearance and behavior), length and weight | 8-55 | 212 |
| Fish | Fish, juvenile growth test | Inhibition of growth | Weight | ≥ 28 | 215 |
| Aquatic plants | Lemna, sp. Growth inhibition test | Inhibition of growth | Frond number, total frond area, dry weight or fresh weight | 7-10 | 221 |

# Chapter 2

# SOIL ASSESSMENT BASED ON
# TOXICITY THRESHOLD

The assessment of soil quality is generally based on the determination of the concentration of pollutants in soils. The estimated concentration is compared with specific threshold values and the degree of contamination is evaluated. Thus, many regulatory bodies all over the world have developed soil quality values. These values can be developed for three main applications:

- Screening values: representing soil concentration levels that may cause potential ecological dysfunction, and therefore, if exceeded, will require a site-specific assessment.
- Cleanup targets: representing the objectives to be achieved in restoration processes. In some cases, these values represent a similar level of protection as the screening values, while in other regulations the decision has to balance the restoration cost against the ecological benefit.
- Intervention values: representing concentrations which are indicative of seriously contaminated sites that require immediate clean-up or control actions.

Some national guides, i.e. Netherlands Guide (The Ministry of Housing, Spatial Planning and the Environment, 2001), Swiss Guide (Hämmann et al., 1998) or Federal Soil Protection Act in German (BbodSchG, 1998) define different standard values covering several of the above mentioned categories. For a long time, SQSs values have been used as a tool to decide the necessity to undertake actions. Nowadays, in many countries the preferred use of SQSs is that of trigger values for site specific investigations, which allow deciding the remedial actions.

In addition, site specific values can be defined taking into account site specific characteristics such as soil properties, climate, etc. Values obtained in this way are more realistic and usually higher than generic soil quality values. Site-specific values in combination with generic values are used by different regulations (e.g. Canada, The Netherlands) as a valuable tool to determine the risk of contaminated soils.

The SQSs are established on risk basis, and they represent the soil concentration that does not exceed a pre-established ecological risk level. Most developed countries have produced technical guidance documents and protocols to conduct environmental risk assessments (ERAs). In Europe, the so-called Technical Guidance Document (TGD) (EC, 2003) developed by experts from the EU countries under the coordination of the European Chemicals Bureau, represents the basic technical guidance for the risk assessment of industrial chemicals. Specific guidelines for several chemical groups, such as pesticides, feed additives, pharmaceuticals and so on, are also available. A review on the scientific bases of the different European ERA protocols was produced in 2003 by a Task Force of the EU Scientific Steering Committee (SSC-European Commission, 2003).

Risk assessment allows predicting the likelihood of an adverse effect to occur; the assessment of chemicals requires the estimation of the expected level of exposure to potentially toxic chemical substances, and the expected consequences for exposed organisms. Thus, environmental risk assessment includes the following aspects: description of potentially adverse effects to the environment (hazard identification) and estimation of the magnitude of these effects (dose-response assessment); determination of receptors potentially exposed and the conditions of exposure (exposure assessment) and finally, estimation of the probability of an adverse effect to occur based on the comparison between effects and exposure (NRC, 1983; Suter et al., 2000) (figure 1). An essential part of any proper risk assessment is the identification of the uncertainties in the analysis.

## 2.1. DETERMINATION OF SOIL QUALITY VALUES

To establish soil quality standards, risk assessment is applied in a backtrack approach, which allows setting the level of one or more chemicals in the soil associated to a certain risk level. Initially, the acceptable risk level is established.

Secondly, the effects on the environment are determined based on toxicity assays. Finally, the exposure levels that satisfy the predetermined risk levels are selected.

Accordantly, the methodology used to determine SQSs involves the following steps: identification of potential pathways for exposure and relevant receptors for soil contaminants (exposure assessment), identification of effects for the selected receptors in the developed scenario (effect assessment) and determination of SQS for the different receptors/compartments assuming a predetermined risk level (risk assessment). These steps can be associated into risk lines, which define the processes involved in the transference of the chemical from soil to the receptor.

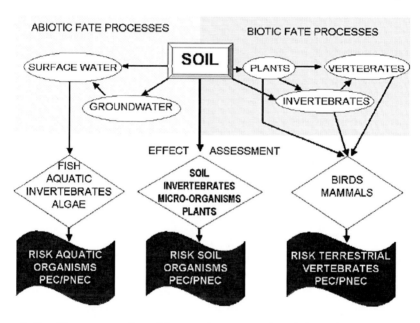

Figure 1. Graphic representation of the generic conceptual model. Symbols represent sources (double square), exposure estimations (ellipses), effect assessments (rhombus) and risk characterization processes (flags).

CONTAMINANT IN SOIL → EXPOSURE PATTERN → RECEPTOR

Different values can be developed depending on the land use patterns. Differences in SQSs for each land use result from the consideration of different levels of protection, different receptors and different exposure pathways. According to some European (Denmark or Switzerland) and non-European authorities (Canadian Council of Ministers of the Environment (CCME) and the Australian EPA) different land uses may not need to support the same diversity of ecological services and functions, and they allow the use of less conservative numbers for commercial, industrial, or residential lands. The Netherlands also defines different land uses, not to modify the values, but to determine if the value for ecological protection should or should not be applied. The approach adopted in Spain considers land uses for human health protection but a single level for ecosystem protection, with regional authorities being responsible for the decision whether to apply or not the ecosystem protection level in each facility depending on the ecological relevance of the area instead of its use pattern. The rationale for this decision is the presence of industrial facilities in areas with ecological values.

## 2.1.1. Exposure Assessment

Exposure assessment defines the amount of substances available to a receptor by the different exposure routes. Based in these environmental routes, different scenarios must be developed to describe the circumstances that determine the level of exposure. For each scenario relevant ecological receptors and exposure routes are selected; then relationships between the soil concentration and the exposure to the receptor are established. Usually, the scenarios are selected representing different land uses.

Model simulations are accepted for exposure analysis, as environmental measurement data are difficult to obtain. The exposure models relate the concentration of a substance in soil to the potential for exposure or uptake by an ecological receptor. Calculated exposure levels are typically called Predicted Environmental Concentration (PEC). The key elements to determine the exposure to a chemical substance are: magnitude, extension and frequency of exposure, and the fate and transport of contaminants from soil. In any exposure model, three key elements must be defined: partitioning of the substance between the soil phases (air, water, soil), transport of the substance to other mediums (e.g. plant or soil organism, air, surface and groundwater) and direct and indirect exposure routes. With this aim, it is necessary to have information of physiochemical properties (vapor pressure, solubility, etc) and ambient behavior (degradation, bioaccumulation, etc) of soil contaminants. However, for many substances transfer and fate data are lacking.

The scenarios are designed to be protective where conditions may lead to highest exposure i.e. worst possible case. In site specific studies, the specific characteristic of the site should be considered to obtain more realistic exposure data.

## 2.1.1.1. Selection of Ecological Receptors

Considering the ecological risk assessment principles (e.g. USEPA, 1998) this aspect is an essential part of the problem and requires a combination of regulatory needs and scientifically based assessment possibilities. Receptors can be selected attending to the land use but it is advisable to define a base set of organisms that would insure a minimum function for any land use. These, usually include plants, soil invertebrates and microorganisms.

Ecological receptors, such as aquatic organisms and terrestrial vertebrates, can be affected by soil pollution through indirect routes. Aquatic communities of water bodies located in the vicinity of the polluted site may be affected by the potential contamination of surface and ground waters due to drainage, leaching and run-off. Terrestrial vertebrates may be affected through the consumption of contaminated plants and invertebrates from the area (secondary poisoning). For a higher tier assessment, the complexity of terrestrial ecosystems should be considered (CSTEE, 2000), and specific conceptual models covering this complexity (Tarazona and Vega, 2002; Tarazona et al., 2002) should be applied.

References to water regulations are common in soil protection policies. However, most of the guides do not integrate protection of aquatic organisms in the determination of soil quality values. In Europe, groundwater protection is considered in ca. 50% of the countries in most of the cases related to human health by the consumption of drinking water. Conversely, surface water is only included in Spain and Sweden. In some cases, surface and ground water are considered at site-specific level (Carlon et al., 2007).

Protection of terrestrial vertebrates is considered in most of the guides. However, in general, critical values for these receptors are limited to herbivorous animals or livestock as in Canadian (http://ec.gc.ca/CEQG-RCQE)or British Columbia (http://www.env.gov.bc. ca/epd/epdpa/contam_sites/guidance) jurisdictions and considered exclusively in the agricultural land use or focused on a species-specific basis as the Australian approach (http://www.epa.gov/ecotox/ecossl/pdf/ecossl_attachment_1-1.pdf). Toxicological relationships are expressed in terms of dietary exposures followed by a variety of methods to estimate a corresponding soil concentration. The bioconcentration factor is used to determine the substance concentration in food. The combination of persistence and potential for bioaccumulation produces and additional hazard: biomagnification through the trophic chain. Biomagnification is considered only in some cases, usually related to persistent substances. Top predators, potentially the most impacted organisms, are the focus of this assessment (Fernández et al., 2006).

## 2.1.2. Effects Assessment

### 2.1.2.1. Toxicity Data

Ecosystem integrity was defined by Cairns (1977) as "the maintenance of both structural and functional characteristic of an ecosystem to ensure that ecological services will be available on a sustained basis". Accordingly, the development of SQSs is intended for the protection of the structure and function of ecosystems. Consequently, the most relevant endpoints to set Soil Quality Values are growth, mortality and reproduction. Regarding the preservation of the ecosystem function, microbial endpoints related to the C- and N-cycle are included. Other parameters such as biomarkers and endpoints related to the mode of action, such as endocrine disruption, can be used to trigger further studies on the effects on population.

Toxicity is by definition the measurement of the adverse effects that a substance provokes on a biological system. Ideally, hazard information would be available for all species. However, this can never be achieved given that thousands of species may be potentially exposed. Therefore, tests are performed on a range of representative species and extrapolations are made to account for differences in species sensitivity. In general, chronic NOEC values for ecologically relevant endpoints (growth and reproduction) are preferred, and acute L(E)50s are employed as surrogates if valid chronic data are not found. Nevertheless, other considerations are possible. Thus, different toxicity data (EC10, EC50, etc) are used according to the intended protection level and hence, different Soil Quality Values are obtained (e.g. Germany).

Data on the effects of substances to organisms can be mainly obtained from data bases (ECOTOX, RAIS, HSDB, RAR, etc.) and studies from research institutes. In addition, industry generates data on the effects on organisms for the notification and registration of substances. All these data must be evaluated regarding to their reliability and relevance. Toxicity data are generated from soils with different properties (e.g. pH, percentage of organic matter, etc.). This means that the results of tests conducted in different soils, with different characteristics, cannot be compared or used for risk assessment as such, but should be normalized to standard conditions. For non-ionic organic compounds the data are normalized on the basis of the soil organic matter content, because it is assumed that the bioavailability for non-ionic substances is determined by the organic matter content only (EC, 2003). For metals and other inorganic substances, the organic matter content is not the only factor influencing the bioavailability, factors such as clay content and the pH of the soil are also important. To set environmental quality objectives for metals, different normalization methods are proposed. For example, in The Netherlands, terrestrial toxicity data for metals are normalized on the basis of clay and/or organic matter content. However, the relationship between soil characteristics and bioavailability of metals is very complex and normalization methods lack sufficient scientific validity to be used for metals.

### 2.1.2.2. Extrapolation

Ecotoxicity data are gathered, screened for their quality and finally, data are extrapolated to cover uncertainties, such as inter- and intra- species variation, extrapolation from subchronic to chronic exposure duration and extrapolation from laboratory to field effects. The commonly used extrapolation procedures are: deterministic methods based on assessment factors and probabilistic approaches based on species sensitivity distributions.

### 2.1.2.2.1. The Deterministic Method

The deterministic method uses the lowest toxicity value plus an assessment factor to cover the remaining uncertainty. The validated toxicity data for the most sensitive taxonomic group in each compartment is divided by the selected assessment factor. In this way, an ecotoxicological threshold-like concentration, called Predicted No Effect Concentration (PNEC) is estimated for the environmental compartment. This is the methodology described in the TGD (EC, 2003) for the chemical assessment. However, others ERA protocols, in Europe or other parts of the world, do not include this step and the risk quotients are directly calculated as ratios between expected concentrations and toxicity endpoints (SSC-European Commission, 2003).

Assessment factors, used in the deterministic method, are frequently used as a generally accepted practice in soil quality assessment (van Straalen and van Gestel, 1993; Jager et al., 1994; Van de Plassche, et al., 1999). The selection of factors is basically a regulatory decision and the European legislation offers examples of largely different factors applied to the same ecotoxicity data (a revision is presented in SSC-European Commission, 2003). The Assessments Factors depend on the availability of data for the taxonomic groups considered for each compartment. They decrease orders of magnitude if chronic data on all relevant taxonomic groups are available. Generally, the assessment factors for PNEC derivation based on laboratory studies ranges from 1000, when only acute values are available, to 10 if chronic NOECs can be found for all relevant taxonomic groups. The assessment factors can be adjusted if new data become available, and must be selected case-by-case if multispecies tests are used. If the availability of data is scarce, high assessment factors must be used which can result in overprotective Soil Quality Standards. This is especially important in the case of a naturally occurring substance where values of SQS may be very near to or within the background range.

### 2.1.2.2.2. The Probabilistic Method

The probabilistic method is based on the species sensitivity distributions (SSD) methodology that uses the whole toxicity data set to elaborate a reliable distribution of the sensitivity of the species to the assessed chemical (Postuma, 2002). The method uses all available data, instead of the most sensitive species, to estimate the distribution curve and the selected percentile. Protection levels are defined in terms of percentage of species to be protected. Consequently, a selected percentile of the species sensitivity distribution is estimated and it is used as the final criterion value (van Straalen and Denneman, 1989; Wagner and Løkke, 1991). The main assumptions of the SSD approach are: the protection of a large part of the structure is enough to protect the ecosystem functions, the distribution of species sensitivities follows a theoretical distribution function, and the group of species tested in the laboratory is a random sample of this distribution. An advantage of this method is that it uses the whole sensitivity distribution of species in an ecosystem to derive a Soil Quality Standard, instead of taking always the lowest effect endpoint. Nevertheless, to apply this methodology a sufficiently large reliable data set for different taxonomic groups is necessary, which in occasions is difficult to obtain. In general, at least 10 NOEC values including different taxonomic groups are required.

The species sensitivity distribution approach has been criticized mainly because it assumes that the protection of the selected percentage of species confers an appropriate level of protection on ecosystem structure and function and because of its lack of validation (OECD, 1992a; Forbes and Forbes, 1993; Smith and Cairns, 1993). Moreover, this approach may not be applicable as such for substances with a specific mode of action.

The SSD approach may be also used to determine PNEC, in a combination of deterministic and probabilistic methods. In this case, a toxicity value protective to a selected percentage of species is considered rather than the lowest toxicity value and an assessment factor, usually between 1 and 5, depending on expert judgment, may be applied. Regardless the theoretical discussions, the real comparisons should consider the overall approaches as a whole, certainly, the deterministic approach selects the most sensitive tested species but from a very limited number of species, while the probabilistic approach may appear as less protective as it is based on a percentile, but from a larger data set, representing a significant reduction in the overall uncertainty. The experience tends to demonstrate that in general the deterministic approach is useful for an initial screening assessment and the SSD approach represents a proper refinement alternative.

## 2.1.3. Risk Assessment

Risk is defined as the estimation of the incidence and severity of the adverse effects likely to occur due to actual or predicted exposure to a substance (Pugh and Tarazona, 1998). SQSs are established on risk basis, and represent the soil concentration that does not exceed a pre-established ecological risk level. A basic problem in the SQSs derivation is to select which levels of risk can be accepted. In countries where different values are defined for different regulatory applications, the level of risk is usually related to the intended use of SQSs. Thus, the need of action (remediation, restrictions in land use, etc) is related to a warning risk; screening values are based on potentially unacceptable risks and target values are based on neglected risk.

In all cases, the exposure is assessed against the effects, according to the maximum permissible risk. In this way, a critical soil concentration associated with the exposure scenario is calculated. Two approaches are possible. In the former (deterministic method), the environmental risk assessment is established for each environmental compartment through the risk characterization ratios (RCRs). These are defined as the ratio between the Predicted Environmental Concentration (PEC) and the Predicted No Effect Concentration (PNEC) for each environmental compartment (water column, soil, wildlife food items). Thus, the development of the soil quality standards followed two steps, first the assessment of the PNEC (or alternative effect assessment) for each compartment; and second, the estimation of the soil concentration which would give an exposure/PNEC ratio of 1. This is the approach followed in the Spanish or Australian regulations.

In the second method, the probabilistic risk assessment "use probabilities or probability distributions to quantify one o more sources of variability and/or uncertainty in exposure and/or effects and the resulting risk" (EUFRAM, 2006). Probabilistic approaches enable variation and uncertainty to be quantified, mainly by using distributions instead of fixed values in risk assessment. A distribution describes the range of possible values of both exposure and toxicity, and shows which values within the range are most likely. The result of risk assessment can also be shown as a distribution, showing the range of environmental impacts that are possible, and which impacts within that range are most likely. This should provide a better basis for decision-making, because the full range of possible outcomes can be taken into account. The SQSs may then represent a fix probability level assumed to be acceptable from a cost/benefit or risk/benefit perspective. In fact this is equivalent to the method used for the human health assessment on non-threshold genotoxic carcinogens.

Up to now, the probabilistic approaches in environmental risk assessment have gain only limited acceptance partly due to a lack of enough knowledge for their use in decision making. Usually, probabilistic tools are used in refinement of exposure and effects at higher tier level. In a single level, the most frequent probabilistic element used is the SSD which are used to represent variation in the sensitivity of different species to a single chemical (Aldenberg et al., 2002). Thus, standards are derived using the percentiles of the distribution, i.e. the concentration that exceeds the toxicity endpoint for a given proportion of species. This value is defined as HCx and represents the concentration of a substance at which x percent of the species in an ecosystem may experience effects. This percentage is a political decision and allows obtaining different values associated to neglected, warning or relevant risk. Thus in The Netherlands the intervention values for ecosystems lie at the serious risk level, i.e. HC50, whereas HC5 is selected for target values (The Ministry of Housing, Spatial Planning and the Environment, 2001). Different values in the range of 5 to 50 percentile are used by different European countries (Carlon et al., 2007).

## 2.2. ENVIRONMENTAL RISK ASSESSMENT FOR METALS

Application of risk assessment methodologies to metal contaminated soils presents a number of problems, due to the especial characteristics of metals that must be accounted:

- Metals are natural occurring substances. Consequently, background concentrations and the exposure due to these background concentrations must be considered in the risk assessment.
- The availability of metals in the soil is highly dependent on soil properties. It is of the utmost importance for the study of exposure and effects assessment.
- Metals can be present in different chemical forms with different chemical and toxicological properties that can be transformed one in other due to environmental changes.
- Some metals are essential elements for metabolism and their levels must be maintained above the deficiency range.

## 2.2.1. Background Levels

Some substances like metals and some chemicals (e.g. PAHs) occur naturally with background concentrations in soils that vary widely. Consideration of background concentrations is essential in SQSs setting and it is the main concern in metals and metalloids. However, characterizing natural background is not easy and must be site-specific.

Countries considering background concentrations in derivation of standard values use different approaches. In some countries it is taken as a reference value, in other countries it is added to the estimated negligible risk concentrations. For example, the reference values for selected metals in soils in the United States are based on the 95th percentile from the frequency distribution (Holmgren et al., 1993; Ryan y Chaney, 1997). In Spain, the mean plus two times the standard deviation of background values, measured in a surrounding clean area can be used as soil quality values if values based in risk assessment have not been described.

Another possibility for the derivation of soil quality values of metals is the application of the "added risk approach" (Struijs et al., 1997; Crommentuijn et al., 1997; Crommentuijn et al., 2000). The use of the added risk approach only considers the anthropogenic amount of substance for the effect assessment of that substance. Thus, a possible contribution of the natural background concentration to toxic effects is ignored. In this way, the risk is determined according to the added metal, based in "added Predicted Environmental Concentration" ($PEC_{add}$) and "added Predicted No Effect Concentration" ($PNEC_{add}$).

In countries where risk assessment is applied to metals, assessment factors used in derivation of SQSs can result in concentrations very near to or within the background range of that naturally occurring substance. In these cases, in most of the countries the average natural background levels are adopted as soil quality standards instead of risk based concentrations.

## 2.2.2. Bioavailability in Metal Risk Assessment

Bioavailability can be broadly defined as the portion of a chemical in the environment that is available for biological action, such as uptake by an organism (Rand, 1995). This fraction is different of the available fraction which can be defined as the fraction of the metal that is extractable from the substrate by chemical (e.g.: neutral salt, water extraction) or physical means (e.g. pore water collection). This fraction is generally considered to be a better estimation as the fraction that is potentially available for organisms, than the total concentration.

The consideration of the bioavailable concentration in the derivation of quality standards would assure a better relation between exposure and effects than the use of total soil concentrations (McLaughlin et al., 2000a, 2000b). Biological availability is often thought to be comparable to chemical availability. However, the bioavailability differs per biological species since it depends on physiological characteristics of the specific organism (exposure route, uptake, etc). Different methods have been used to determine the available fraction: free metal ion activity (Parker and Pedler, 1997), pore-water concentration (Peijnenburg et al. 1997) or the amount of metals extracted using different extraction methods (Adriano, 2001). The bioaccumulation of contaminants in organisms can serve also as a measure of the bioavailability of metals in soil (Van Gestel et al., 2002). A review of the assessment of the bioavailability of metals in different organisms is presented by Hund-Rinke and Kördel (2003).

It has been generally accepted that the phytoavailability of a metal is related to the free ion activity of that metal in solution and that soluble metal-ligand complexes are not readily taken up (Parker and Pedler, 1997). However, in some cases recent findings indicate that activity of the free ion does not always correlate well with availability. Complexation of metals with inorganic or organic ligands in soils can increase plant uptake of metals (McLaughlin et al., 2000b). Moreover, metal free ion activity in an aqueous phase or extract is not a good measure of bioavailability when the exposure is not through the aqueous phase (Janssen et al., 1997).

The difficulty of using soil pore water concentration to determine the bioavailable concentration is that it is difficult to measure and highly variable in temporal and spatial dimensions. Moreover, its use should be limited to those species for which the pore water is the dominant uptake route, as microorganisms and some plant species Other soil dwelling organisms may be also exposed via a combination of uptake routes, such as pore water, food, and direct ingestion of soil (Lock and Janssen, 2001, 2003a).

The chemical extraction technique is the most commonly used method to estimate the fraction of a metal that is bioavailable in the short term. Numerous studies have been performed to estimate bioavailable pool in soils, being the most aimed to relate metal soil speciation and plant uptake (Adriano, 2001). Good correlations between plant uptake and chemical fractions have been obtained using dilute acids (HCl, $H_2SO_4$, $NH_4OAc$, etc) and chelating agents such as EDTA o DTPA. However, there is no universal soil extractant that can be used to estimate metal bioavailability. This is because of the complexity of metal ion dynamics in the soil system, environmental factors and mainly, differences between organisms.

A recent advance in the application of bioavailability in the metal risk assessment is the development of Terrestrial Biotic Ligand Model (TBLM). The Biotic Ligand Model (BLM) has been used to develop water quality criteria and perform aquatic risk assessment for metals (Di Toro et al., 2001). This method allows evaluating quantitatively the manner in which water chemistry affects the speciation and biological availability of metals in aquatic systems. Consequently, it allows reducing the toxicity variation due to differences in metal bioavailability. Likewise, the TBLM predict soil toxicity according with metal speciation and soil properties. This method is able to achieve a normalization of the wide variation in toxicological endpoints among soils of different properties and can provide a framework for modeling metals ecotoxicity in soils (Koster, et al., 2006; Thakali, 2006a, 2006b) .

Within the EU, the risk assessment strategies for metals such as zinc or copper are developing alternatives to consider bioavailability in soil risk assessment, following equivalent methods to the Biotic Ligand Model (BLM), which has been used to develop water quality criteria and perform aquatic risk assessment for metals. The combination of these models with the effect background concentrations on the organism responses may produce significant advances in future years.

In the mean time, another approach to the problem is to use the weakly adsorbed and easy extractable fraction rather than the bioavailable fraction in the risk assessment. Soil risk assessment of metals is based on laboratory toxicity tests which are performed in soils freshly spiked with metal salts. However, in the field, metal availability decreases with time, mainly due to aging processes (Ma et al., 2005; Song et al., 2006). Thus, the use of toxicity data obtained with spiked soils can result in an over estimation of the hazard of metal contaminated soils (Lock and Janssen, 2003b: Oorts et al. 2007). An approach to this problem is to define an extraction solution, which is able to extract the weakly adsorbed and easy extractable fraction. This approach could be an alternative to the use of the bioavailable fraction as this chemical fraction would be independent from biological availability which in fact is species-specific.

## 2.3. MAIN PROBLEMS IN DERIVATION OF SOIL QUALITY STANDARDS

The aim of risk assessment is the protection of the structure and function of the ecosystems. However, there is not enough information of which endpoints are critical and relevant for the ecosystem. As an alternative this protection is based on toxicity to some selected organisms, determined using toxicity assays. In order to relate effects to the observed concentrations, a large amount of ecotoxicological information is necessary, which is restricted actually, to a few priority pollutants. The lack of enough toxicity data for many substances and the necessity of applying the assessment factor lead to an overestimation of risk.

Soil quality assessment based on standards does not allow an integration of combined effects of contaminants in soil. Thus, synergic and antagonic effects between substances that can modify the toxicity of pollutants in soil are not considered, with some exceptions as some family of compounds with a similar mechanism of toxicity (e.g. chlorophenols) which have SQSs based on the sum of concentrations.

The determination of exposure also presents uncertainties related to the identification of possible routes of exposure and the parameters used to predict the exposure concentration by the indirect routes. Exposure is usually obtained using conservative assumptions that may overestimate the risk. A problem of special concern is addressing the bioavailability in the definition of SQSs. As indicated above, efforts are being made in order to account for the bioavailability of a substance in the prediction of risk.

An added problem is the differences in Soil Quality Standards among countries. In spite of using common methodologies, different soil quality values are defined by the different countries. Differences are mainly due to: regulatory application of the value or values suggested as triggers, land use dependence, selection of ecological receptors (mainly inclusion of aquatic organisms and terrestrial vertebrates, and particularly wild species), consideration of fate processes such as mobilization or biomagnification and the data extrapolation method. International harmonization of Soil Quality Standards was discussed in the concerted actions CARACAS (Ferguson et al., 1998) and CLARINET 2 (Vegter et al., 2003). Presently, the EU is making efforts in order to achieve similar values for the implementation of the Framework Soil Directive.

*Chapter 3*

# TIER LEVEL METODOLOGIES FOR RISK ASSESSMENT

Risk assessment is usually conducted as a tiered process performed in several steps. The initial steps, covering screening and lower tier risk assessments are based on the precautionary principle, worst-cases are assumed and the spatial and temporal variability is basically not considered. In higher risk assessments, all the available information is used and the specific characteristics of the site are considered to determine the actual risk, if possible in a quantized form and including the evaluation of the remaining uncertainties. The tier approach offers decision making at each level, when the risk is low, no additional efforts are required, when the risk is potentially high, the information required for the subsequent levels must be produced and analyzed. Thus, the degree of uncertainty decreases, while reliability increases. Derivation of generic SQSs is based on simplified risk assessments and the values obtained tend to be overprotective in most of the cases. Usually, these values are also considered as a first step within a tiered approach for decision-making. The following steps consist in data refinement producing a more realistic assessment, in order to allow exonerating sites considered potentially contaminated according to conservative values, or the confirmation of the potential risk.

Tiered protocols have been developed for environmental risk assessment of chemicals (SSC- European Commission, 2003) and pesticides (Campbell et al., 1999; Giddings et al., 2002), mainly aimed at aquatic organisms. There are different methodologies for risk refining, being all of them based in two approaches: i) the use of probabilistic assumptions to cover variability and ii) the use of more complex exposure and/or effect tools to obtain more realistic situations. According to SSC-European Commission (2003), higher tier protocols can be grouped in five levels to refine exposure and five levels to refine effects. The combination of both is also possible. These methodologies can be applied to refine SQSs, obtaining less overprotective and more realistic values. Moreover, in some regulations (e.g. Canada, Spain), screening values may be modified attending to the information collected in a particular site. This information is mainly referred to those physicochemical characteristics affecting chemicals transfer from soil to the aquatic compartment and the terrestrial vertebrates and a selection of relevant receptors in the site (figure 2). Values which are obtained considering the specific characteristics of the assessed site are referred to as Specific Soil Quality Values (SSQSs) and may be used for the characterization of soils in the site for which they were developed, instead of SQSs.

The refinement process itself is iterative, and based on cost/efficiency estimations. The refinement may focus on the exposure or on the effect sides, or directly in a combination of both approaches, depending on the cost estimations and the likelihood for excluding/confirming risks for each applicable tool. Although this chapter describes the refinement process in terms of subsequent steps, form lower to higher complexity; in reality, the process must be decided case by case. Thus, it is possible to move directly from the screening to the top level if required.

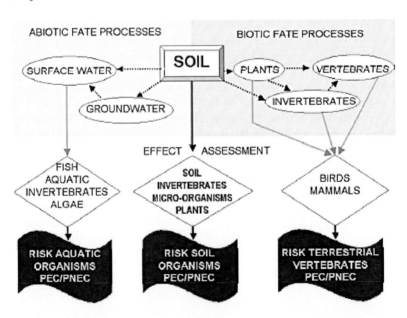

Figure 2. Adaptation of the generic model for site-specific assessments based on site conditions (non continuous lines) and ecological relevance (open arrows).

## 3.1. High Tier Exposure Assessment

The exposure refinement may be conducted following different steps, which have not necessarily to be applied sequentially. As explained above, the site characteristics allow deciding which refinement tool is more adequate.

### 3.1.1. Level 1. Generic Screening Scenarios

This level constitutes an initial screening evaluation using the least possible information. Threshold values are estimated based on very conservative exposure assumptions. For example, 100% bioavailability is assumed, wildlife is estimated to consume 100% of their diet from the site, and invertebrates are assumed to be stationary in the contaminated portion of the soil. The highest reasonably possible exposure is calculated considering it is constant in time and homogenous in space.

### 3.1.2. Level 2. Probabilistic Generic Scenarios

At this level, the parameters represented by single data are replaced in the models by the probabilistic estimations. That is, individual data for the variables are substituted by their distribution function, which can be obtained using statistical analysis. The use of distributions as input parameters allows producing the likelihood for the exposure levels as probabilities, as well as, variation and uncertainty in exposure; using tools such as the Monte Carlo analyses. A key step is identifying the main factors and the mechanism that influence the exposure and how they interact.

Distributions may be used to refine some aspects of exposure assessment for aquatic and terrestrial organisms (EC, 2002a; EC. 2002b), to determine the proportion of exposures exceeding some given concentration (e.g. a toxicity endpoint) or to determine the variability and uncertainty within a route of exposure (e.g. concentration of contaminant in the diet of birds of mammals).

## 3.1.3. Level 3. Realistic Scenarios Considering Spatial and Temporal Variability

At this level, more realistic scenarios are defined, considering relevant receptors and site-specific characteristics affecting the exposure level. Thus, the relevant ecological receptors in the site and compartments that can be affected by soil pollution are selected. Three types of ecological receptors may be affected by soil contamination: soil dwelling organisms, aquatic communities from water bodies located in the vicinity of the polluted site and terrestrial vertebrates. All of these compartments are usually considered in a generic scenario. However, specific site characteristics might be unnecessary considering some of these receptors. On the other hand, some species may require additional protection due to socio/economic or ecotoxicological reasons (e.g. endangered species where individual protection is required to maintain biodiversity).

Regarding exposure level, three factors should be considered, the application of models using specific-site characteristics, the bioavailability of contaminants and the spatial and temporal variability in the exposure level. Initially, the exposure levels coming from indirect routes are determined using models and equations. Depending on the type of assessment, the estimation may focus on worst- and/or realistic-case conditions and use measured or default values. The transfer of chemicals from soil to water and food is usually calculated using partitioning coefficients between different compartments (soil, air, water, food) and standard soil characteristics (organic matter content, bulk density, etc). Default values can be substituted in the equations by site specific values, and Soil Quality Values can be recalculated to obtain Specific Soil Quality Values. In many cases, one limitation is that, equations to obtain SQS are not presented in a transparent way, hence it may be difficult to modify the default conditions to include site-specific characteristics.

Exposure from water can be refined using different models. Many models have been developed to calculate the movement of contaminants through soils. Parkhurst and Appelo, 1999; PELMO (Klein, 1991), PEARL (Leistra et al., 2000) ;etc.). Models simulate the process of transfer from soil to water that can occur in the soil. Its reliability depends on the suitability of the modeled process to actual situation, the equations used to determine the effects and the value of the parameter selected for the model. The application of models requires a sufficient physicochemical characterization of the soil, which is not possible in a generic scenario. At this level, the dilution factors occurring in the site may be considered and models may be applied to estimate the transfer of contaminants from soil to water. An alternative source of information are leaching tests (OCDE, 2004d) performed in the laboratory using standard methods. These tests are relatively short, reproducible and cost-effective methods to estimate the mobility of contaminants in the soil.

Exposure due to the consumption of contaminated food can be also corrected. For example, the determination of secondary poisoning based in worst-case estimations assumes that wildlife consumes 100% of their diet from the site. This is an unrealistic case. Exposure may be corrected to include the real consumption of food. This consumption may be estimated taking into account the time that the organisms stay in the site, which depends on the size of the habitat for this specie. These data can be obtained by radio tracking or visual observations of birds and mammals (EU, 2002). Data from radio tracking studies is obviously the most useful, but it is also the most difficult and expensive to obtain. On the other hand, the time that the organisms stay in the site depends on the size of the habitat for this specie. The quotient between habitat size and surface of the contaminated site is an appropriate factor for an initial correction of expected exposure through the contaminated food. Additional refinement can be obtained through the methodology applied by the European Food Safety Authority (EFSA) for the higher tier assessment of pesticides. The method considers the selection of key species for each site and the identification of food consumption items on the basis of the species metabolic requirements.

The consideration of the bioavailable concentration provides a more appropriate measure of exposure compared to the use of total soil concentration, and should be included in the exposure refinement. Different approaches described in section 3.2.2. to determine the available fraction, such as the use of the extractant solution, the soil pore water concentration, etc. can be applied. For very persistent and bioaccumulation substances, studies must be designed to properly address the potential biomagnification and bioconcentration risk. Studies must cover the potential risk associated with continued or repeated exposures at different trophic levels. The biomagnification risk is considered a key part of the assessment and all potential exposure routes should be considered.

In this level, variations in the exposure level due to time and space changes are considered in the estimation of exposure concentration. In soils, unlike waters, variations in space are more important than variations in time. The spatial consideration may be presented through non-specific or through geo-referenced methods. The first approach requires a lower level of information but the gradients are presented in generic terms not associated to specific locations.

## 3.1.4. Level 4. Semi Field and Field Studies

Models for exposure scenarios are based in the results obtained in the laboratory assays. These assays do not allow considering some factors occurring in the environment. Semi field and field studies allow more realistic estimations of exposure. The main advantage of the semi-field and field studies is that they are based on a realistic level of complexity. The studies cover specific aspects for refining model estimations. Obviously, the best approach is to conduct the studies within the assessed facility; however, the extrapolation of study outcomes between related field conditions may also offer a proper refinement. Almost any parameter or variable can be studied in the field on soil collected at the facility. These include those factors affecting bioavailability and aging processes.

## 3.1.5. Level 5. Exposure Assessment Based on Real Measurement

Almost any investigation aimed to characterize soil contamination is based on direct measurements of pollutants in soil. However, the monitoring efforts can also be applied to other samples. Direct exposure measurement instead of model predictions may be used to determine exposure to soil pollutants by indirect routes: in particular for the aquatic compartments (surface and ground waters) and terrestrial vertebrates feeding in the site. For example, for terrestrial vertebrates protection, the concentration in the food item is estimated from the soil-earthworm and the soil-plant bioconcentration factor (BCF) (Romijn et al., 1994). The estimation of the concentration of the contaminant in plants and terrestrial invertebrates using BCFs may be substituted by the direct measurement of the concentration of the substance in plants and invertebrates. As the uncertainties associated to those models are relatively high, this alternative may offer a quite significant level of refinement and uncertainty reduction.

## 3.2. HIGH TIER EFFECTS ASSESSMENT

The objective is to achieve toxicity values close to actual toxicity thresholds, as well as to determine those endpoints that are relevant for the ecosystem. Effects refinement consists in getting more information in order to obtain more realistic SQSs, mainly due to a reduction of uncertainty. Moreover, the specific characteristics of the site influencing the effects may be included in the performance of assays, which allows obtaining more consistent SSQSs. In the schema 1, higher tier protocols to refine effects on ecosystems, grouped in five levels according to SSC-European Commission (2003) are shown.

## 3.2.1. Level 1. Effects on Single-Species. Deterministic Approach

In this level, risk assessment is based in the deterministic approach carrying out the single-species tests on species selected to cover a minimum of taxonomic groups and assessment factors to account for several forms of uncertainty. In this way, PNECs which are expected to be protective for the concerned compartment, are obtained. More realistic PNEC can be obtained by improving the set of toxicity data. The testing of mores species reduces the uncertainty attributable to inter-species differences in sensitivity and a lower assessment factor may be applied. Likewise, the increase of chronic against acute data to soil and aquatic organisms, and the increase of the exposure time in the assays for terrestrial vertebrates allow decreasing assessment factors applied for short-term to long-term/chronic toxicity extrapolation.

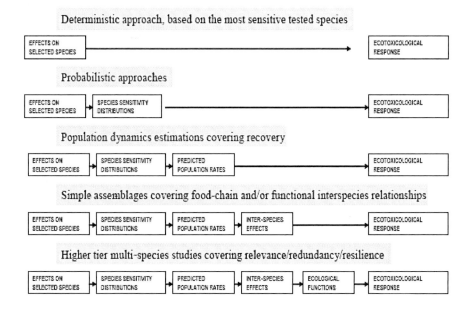

Scheme 1. Higher tier protocols to refine effects on ecosystems, grouped in five levels according to SSC (2003).

In most of the regulations, ecotoxicity data are normalized to standard soils taking into account the organic matter content in the case of organic substances, and the organic matter content and clay in the case of metals. Toxicity values may be modified to account actual soil properties of the site.

## 3.2.2. Level 2. Effects on Single-species. Probabilistic Approach

The probabilistic method most frequently used to refine effects is the SSD approach, although distributions may be also used to determine other types of variability and uncertainty in the effects assessment. In SSDs, the whole data set is used to elaborate a reliable distribution of the sensitivity of the species to the assessed chemical, unlike the deterministic method, which uses the lowest toxicity value. Two approaches are possible to obtain the species sensitivity distribution. The first consists in estimating SSD separately for each taxonomic group, which can be combined if similarities are observed. The second (TGD) consists in determining SSD using at least ten different species covering at least eight taxonomic groups. Efforts are in progress to validate these models, especially to extrapolate SSD values for the protection of the community and the ecosystem. This method requires a larger amount of data representing a wide spectrum of genera. It is necessary to obtain information for a higher number of species performing additional single-species tests in order to apply the model. Some criticisms of probabilistic approaches were made by Forbes and Forbes, 1993.

It should be noted that the whole concept of the use of SSDs for setting ecotoxicological thresholds has been derived for the aquatic compartment, where all assays are structural endpoints and therefore requires some adaptations when extrapolated to the soil/terrestrial environment (e.g. EC, 2003). The soil assessment includes functional parameters in order to the effects on soil microbial populations. Some guidelines, including the European TGD, recommend the derivation of two complementary distributions, one for structural points (plants and invertebrates) and the other for functional endpoints (soil microorganisms). However, when the actual data used for setting the microbial function distribution are considered, it is observed that actually, the assessment does not describe the distribution of the effects of the chemical on microbial processes, but the distribution observed for the same processes among different soil microbial communities. In fact, the data usually cover just three different microbial-mediated processes, each representing the effects on a different sub-group of soil microbial communities:

- Respiration, or C-mineralization, offers a generic assessment covering potential effects on almost the whole community.
- N-mineralization refers exclusively to a very specific group of species which are involved in the different elements of the N mineralization process such as nitrification or ammonification.
- The enzymatic activities cover potential effects on subgroups of species within the microbial community, with significant taxonomic differences depending on the soil and the measured enzyme.

Thus, the distribution offers the responses of different soil communities to the same endpoints, representing in reality a distribution of "community sensitivities" which is therefore comparable to the SSD concept.

## 3.2.3. Level 3. Populations

This refinement level is also based in single-species assays, but toxicity tests are performed in more realistic conditions. The assays intend to predict the ecological relevance of the effects. Thus, more realistic conditions of exposure are included in the assays (e.g. assays that include different routes of exposure). In addition, studies on population effects, biomarkers and endpoints related to the mode of action such as endocrine disruption, may be used as toxicity parameters.

An aspect which is usually evaluated at this level is the study of recovery after the exposure. Time assay is extended to allow species recovering. Effects may be considered of low ecological significance if recovery takes place in a given time period. Recovery may be very different according to the reproduction characteristics of the species. Consequently, a main problem of recovery studies is extrapolating the potential for recovery to other species with different ecological strategies. This is particularly relevant when assessing soil pollution, as typically the contamination is not homogeneously distributed within the facility but presents severe spatial differences. When the pollution is concentrated in hot-spots or presents gradients from certain point sources the overall effect should be assessed at the population level. Models to study the effects on populations, such as Predictive Population Dynamic (Ducrot et al., 2007; Lewis and Law, 2007), may be applied.

## 3.2.4. Level 4. Effects on Communities

Toxicity effects occurring on a species can affect other related species. In this level, species interactions are considered to predict effects at the community level. Single-species assays used in previous levels are substituted by multispecies assays that account for species interactions unlike single-species assays. Multispecie assays are laboratory tests performed in systems denominated microcosms. These systems reproduce part of a terrestrial or aquatic ecosystem and the effects on different organisms are simultaneously studied. Moreover, the exposure conditions may be selected to reproduce the actual conditions. The most used aquatic microcosms reproduces a simplified trophic chain (alga, daphnia, fish). In soils, microcosms include different taxonomic groups (e.g. microorganisms, terrestrial invertebrates and plants).

Aquatic multi-species test systems have been successfully used to assess effects of substances, specially plant protection products, under realistic exposure conditions. Comparable terrestrial use is less developed. However, efforts are directed to prove their application in higher tier assessments. (Fernández et al., 2004; Weyers et al., 2004; Boleas, 2005a; 2005b).

## 3.2.5. Level 5. Effects on Ecosystems

The aim of risk assessment is to protect the structure and function of the ecosystems. The most direct means of studying the effects on ecosystems are mesocosms and field assays. They allow identifying relevant effects, under simulated field conditions. Mesocosms offer the same advantages as microcosms, but the usually include a wider range of species and generally offer a greater potential to assess the response at the highest level of organization. Furthermore natural fluctuations in climatic conditions enhance the level of field realisms. In particular, they enhance the probability of recovery of some species through e.g. colonization. Mesocosms have been developed to study substance effects in the aquatic medium (Campbell et al., 1999; Giddings et al., 2002). They reproduce an aquatic ecosystem from a lagoon, which acts as a biodiversity reservoir. Mesocosms include several hundred of species. They allow the direct measure of ecological parameters affecting population dynamics, biodiversity, nutrients and energy cycles, etc. They represent an intermediate between closely controlled laboratory tests and extensive, loosely controlled field trials (Ramade, 1992; Crossland, 1994). The use of mesocosm-level studies in soil/terrestrial assessment is less common than for the soil environment, but some possibilities have been investigated (Robidoux et al., 2004a; 2005).

Field assays consist in the application of test substance in the fields under controlled conditions, monitoring those parameters that represent the ecosystem structure and function. This assessment provides the most relevant data. In contrast to laboratory tests, rigid protocols are not desirable for field studies. The trial should rather be designed individually addressing the problems that have been identified.

The main limitation for the application of these assays in risk assessment is the extrapolation of results, due to the limited understanding of ecological effects and their poor reproducibility. Results of field studies should be carefully interpreted to determine which observed effects should be considered ecologically significant. The assessment is particularly complex when the spatial distribution of the contaminants in the soil compartment is highly variable.

## 3.3. HIGH TIER RISK CHARACTERIZATION

At single level for risk characterization, the estimated concentration in environmental compartments (PEC) is compared with the estimated concentration below which unacceptable effects on organisms will most likely not occur (PNEC). If the PEC/PNEC > 1, there is potential concern for the environment compartment and risk refinement or risk mitigation measures must be applied. At high tier level, probabilistic methods are usually applied. Two cases are possible to compare the outputs of exposure and effects refinement: i) exposure or effects is represented by a distribution, and the other by point estimation and ii) both, exposure and effects are represented by a distribution. In the first case, the combination of a distribution of toxicities with a specific/set level of exposure characterizes the risk for that level of exposure. Likewise, combining an exposure distribution with point toxicity, characterizes risk as the proportion of concentrations that exceed that toxic threshold, or a set of ecologically relevant endpoint (figure 3).

In the second case, both, exposure and effects are represented by a distribution. The simplest way to combine them is to plot them on a single graph. The extent of the overlap between the two graphs gives a visual impression of the risk: the more the overlap, the higher the risk. Finally, using Monte Carlo analyses it is possible to obtain probability distributions of different risk quotients. For a review of probabilistic risk assessment see http://ww.eupra.com and from the EPA htthp://ww.epa.gov/oppefed1/ecorisk).

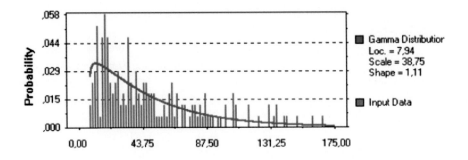

Figure 3. Example of probabilistic assessment. Frequency distribution of soil raw data, adjustment to a probabilistic distribution, and comparison with the PNEC for setting the exceeded level.

*Chapter 4*

# SOIL ASSESSMENT BASED ON DIRECT (ECO)TOXICITY ASSESSMENT (DTA). BIOASSAYS

The risk assessment of soils is mainly based on chemical analyses of toxic pollutants included in priority lists. The soil concentrations measured are compared with threshold values and the degree of contamination is evaluated. However, a classification based exclusively on chemical analysis does not take into account several essential aspects; particularly, mixed toxicity, the toxicity of chemicals not included in the selection of contaminants to be analyzed, and bioavailability. Bioassays provide an alternative, which covers these gaps, as they integrate these effects providing an overall estimation of the soil toxicity to non-acclimated organisms, and further information on bioavailability and interactions (synergism and antagonism) between substances in the mixture. As bioassays determine the toxicity of all contaminants in the soil sample, the method provides an additional guarantee to check that all relevant substances were identified and included in the chemical analyses. This selection is usually based on the historical use of the site, the confirmation from bioassays is essential when this information is uncertain or does not cover the whole history of the facility.

Bioassays are recommended for the estimation of the risk to ecological receptors associated with contaminants in soils (Loibner et al., 2003; Stephenson et al., 2002; Eom et al., 2007). Thus, they have been employed as a complement to chemical analysis in soil monitoring programs for assessment (Maxam et al., 2000) and remediation (Salanitro et al., 1997; Mendonca and Picado, 2002) purposes. However, the inclusion of these assays for soil assessment in regulations is still scarce. In our knowledge, only in Spain, bioassays are included in the regulation (Tarazona et al. 2005) and allow classifying a soil as polluted based exclusively on the results of direct toxicity testing. In other countries the combination of bioassays and chemical analysis is recommended for the site-specific risk assessment (e.g. TRIAD approach for assessing site-specific ecological risks in NL, UK or USA (Long and Chapman, 1985; Burton et al. 2002a; Burton et al. 2002b). In addition, the risk of contaminants leaching from soils into groundwater is required by different legislations (The Netherlands, Spain) in order to determine their impact in the aquatic compartment. The bioassays may cover both, soils and leachates.

Bioassays may be used in a screening phase for a fast identification of polluted sites or for a complete ecotoxicological evaluation. Moreover, they represent valuable monitoring tools to evaluate the effectiveness of remediation processes. The main problem of using bioassays is the sensitivity of the selected methods. Assays performed with environmental samples allow the identification of polluted soils but may be inadequate to decide when a soil has a low risk as the additional assessment factor employed to set the threshold cannot be incorporated in the assessment, and the fact that acute (short-term) bioassays can be easily incorporated, while the inclusion of long-term chronic tests is controversial in terms of viability and cost. Moreover, bioassays do not identify substances causing toxicity. It can be a limitation in the remediation processes since the selected technique depends on the characteristics of the pollutants in the mixture.

An important step in soil quality assessment should be correlating chemical concentrations to effects measured with bioassays. If toxicity cannot be explained attending to the concentration of chemical substances in the soil determined by chemical analysis, further investigations into causal agents of toxicity should be performed. However, in occasions, to relate toxic response from bioassays to the concentration measured through chemical analyses may be difficult, mainly if combined toxicity occurs.

## 4.1. METHODS OF ECOTOXICITY ASSAY

There are different possibilities to study toxicity with environmental samples. The most widely used method consists in laboratory tests, where organisms are exposed to potentially polluted soils that are collected in the study site and transferred to the laboratory. However, other possibilities to assess soil quality by means of toxicity analysis of environmental samples are possible. Intact soil cores may be transferred to the laboratory and toxic effects may be tested to indigenous biota under controlled laboratory conditions. Another way consists in taking organisms from the site and studying them in the laboratory to determine the bioconcentration, biochemical and physiological effects, etc. Finally, in situ biological monitoring analyzes various parameters of natural populations studying how they are affected by exposure to contaminants and determining the ecological quality of a site (Hopkin, 1993; Beck et al., 2005; Römbke et al., 2005). Although the last studies may be considered more realistic, their implementation presents additional complexities and have a main weakness, as pollution represents previous historical releases, the biological community found at the facility has been adapted to or selected by the pollutants, and therefore may be unrepresentative of the natural population expected for equivalent unpolluted sites. In this chapter, the term bioassay is used for toxicity assays performed in the laboratory with selected organisms.

Bioassays on soil samples may be performed using two approaches. In the former, samples are diluted with a non-contaminated control or reference soil and different soil concentrations are tested. In this way, a dose-response similar to that obtained when assaying pure chemical substances is obtained. In the second approach, assays are performed with non-diluted samples. The approaches can be combined or selected on the basis of the expected level of pollution. The results of the toxicity assessment are compared to either a non-polluted control or a clean reference sample and expressed using conventional methods such as percent of inhibition respect to the control, Toxic Units, or the equivalent to the L(E)Cx or NOEC expressed in terms of dilution. The first approach is fast and cheap and allows obtaining directly the toxicity results as a percentage of inhibition between 0 and 100% for each sample. In the dose-response method various dilutions must be tested to obtain the L(E)C50 equivalent value, requiring a higher number of replicates and being more expensive. Moreover, the L(E)C50 values may not be obtained if the sample does not present enough ecotoxicity. However, the use of different concentrations allows obtaining additional information about the risk of contaminated soil. Bioavailable pollutants may be released in the environment due to significant changes in soil properties. This fact is particularly important during soil remediation. In the dose-response approach, the dilution processes modify the bioavailability of chemicals in the soil covering risk due the potential bioavailability changes. In addition, assays at low exposure levels allow determining the risk of spreading the contamination to other areas due to surface movement of contaminated soil caused by erosion, flooding, etc. Regarding data analyses, correctly applied, regression models provide estimations of the parameters of interest with higher sensitivity and precision than analyses at a single dose. Moreover, the use of different concentrations allows detecting cross effects such as hormesis or effects due to different physicochemical properties of the test and control soil.

In both approaches, the effects observed for contaminated samples are usually compared with data obtained from control or reference soils, and significant differences are estimated using statistical analyses. A key point in the soil assessment is the selection of a control or reference soil. Organism toxicity can vary with soil characteristics and selecting an unsuitable reference soil may result in erroneous data. In the ideal case, the reference soil should differ from the contaminated soil only by the absence of pollution. Thus, reference soils are sampled at a non-polluted localization close to the contaminated site. When it is not possible, a reference soil with pH, soil organic matter content, soil texture and nutrients comparable to the test soil should be selected. The selection of a proper reference soil is particularly critical for sublethal endpoints such as reproduction or growth. Texture, nutrients availability, etc may be so influential in the control response that the differences related to the presence of toxic chemicals in the sample can be masked or overestimated.

In addition to soil testing using soil organisms, aquatic organisms have been often used to assess soil toxicity based on the assumption that the chemicals affect the soil organisms via the aqueous phase (Hammel et al., 1998; Bispo et al., 1999). However, this method does not seem correct mainly because it assumes that the sensitivity of terrestrial organisms is similar to that of aquatic organisms. Soil quality tests should focus on soil dwelling organisms (Maxam et al., 2000; Van Gestel et al., 2001; Eom, et al., 2007; Leitgib et al., 2007), while aquatic tests on soil leachates should be used for the risk assessment of contaminated soils to ground and surface waters.

Leachates preparation is a crucial step in the assessment of soil toxicity. Leaching tests may be divided into three kinds: batch tests, column tests and field tests. The leachant used in most of the tests is distilled or de-ionized water, however, the nature of the leachant may vary depending on the purpose for which the test was developed. The batch test consists in shaking a sample of the soil to be assessed during a certain time period, defined shaking conditions and a specified volume of leachant. The main variables in this test are the liquid to solid ratio, the time and potency of the shaking method, and the leachant used in the assay. Different standard leaching methods have been developed for soil assessment (e.g. DIN 38414). The soil to liquid ratio ranges between 1:2 and 1:10. In most of methods, water is the solvent selected and a 10:1 is the most frequently proposed liquid to soil ratio. The column test consists in passing the leachant through a column filled with the soil. This method allows selecting assay conditions which are representative of the environmental situation being assessed.

The variables which affect the assay are the column size, and the flow and characteristics of the leachant. The leaching test may be also performed in lysimeters under field conditions. The leachates obtained may be used for chemical analyses or ecotoxicological tests, providing information on transfer of contaminants from soil to water. Leachates tests are performed by comparing test data to a blank. However, effects due to nutrients in the soil (e.g. growth-stimulating effect on algae) can hide the toxic effects of soil contaminants. This phenomenon may be avoided by relating test data to the leachate from an appropriate reference soil rather than standard blanks normally used in these tests.

## 4.2. TEST ORGANISMS

The application of a set of assays with different organisms is necessary in order to provide an accurate assessment of environmental quality (Greene et al., 1989; Keddy, 1995, Maxam, et al. 2000); due to the different sensitivity of the organism to the various contaminants (Bierkens et al., 1998). Soil protection is usually not directed to protect the structure (composition of the soil biocenosis) but to protect the soil functions. The main functions of soils are the ones associated with organic matter decomposition, nutrients cycle and synthesis of humic compound. The vegetation coverage and the contribution of soil organisms to the soil texture are also relevant. Every function may be performed by different species (functional redundancy). Therefore, the protection of soil functions is guaranteed if the ecological structure is maintained. However, changes in ecological structure do not necessarily mean loss of function.

Bacteria and fungi play an essential role in the decomposition of organic residues. Other organisms such as mites, springtails (Collembolan), isopods, mollusks, millipedes and earthworms, which disturb soil by ingestion or burrowing, influence soil core structure and texture. Earthworms are the best-known group with an important role in maintaining structure and soil fertility. Soil fauna also contributes to the decomposition process directly or indirectly through soil aeration and by breaking down leaf material into smaller particles, which are more easily decomposed by microbes etc. Finally, plants are the most prominent primary producers in all ecosystems. Moreover, they contribute to soil fertility and structure, regulate the potential for erosion, run-off and water behavior, and define habitats for wildlife.

Ideally, the toxicity of all ecological or commercially important organisms living in or associated to the soil should be tested. However, this is not possible and a small number of assays are selected to cover as much as possible the ecosystem risk. The test organisms selected should be representative of the functional roles played by the organisms encountered in the field and sensitive to the contaminants. The organisms are selected attending to the relevance of the species, the sensitivity of the tests and the simplicity and the costs of the assays. Different toxicity tests have been developed for the assessment of chemical substances and have been standardized by several associations (OECD; ISO, ASTM, DIN, AFNOR, EPA, etc) and may be applied to the assessment of soil samples. There are many different ways to measure toxicity. Biochemical, physiological, reproductive and behavioral effects can provide toxicity data. However, in direct toxicity assays, the usually measured parameters are lethality, reproduction and growth. These parameters are considered to be relevant for the estimation of field effects. A review of the toxicity tests available for ecotoxicity assessment of contaminated sites was compiled by Stephenson et al. (2002).

The most widely used tests with soil invertebrates include earthworms, springtails (Collembolan), enchytraeids and isopods (Callow, 1993). The assays with earthworm are the best established and are used as legislative requirement for the risk assessment of chemical substances. Two earthworm tests, which measure effects on mortality and reproduction, using E*isenia sp.* have been standardized by the OECD (2004a). Other sublethal effects such as avoidance, loss of weight, etc may be measured. The bioconcentration of chemical in earthworms can also be determined and used to predict the exposure of predators through the food.

Collembolans are used in many laboratories to assess the effect of chemicals, although these assays have not got such an advanced legislative stage as earthworms. Collembolans are among the most abundant arthropods. Most species consume fungi in soil and leaf litter. The most widely used specie of Collembolan is a parthenogenetic strain of *Folsomia candida* (ISO, 1999). The effects on reproduction are used as endpoint. However, future testing methods involve the use of more sensitive endpoints such as locomotor activities, behavior, avoidance of contaminated food and effects on population growth rates (Fountain and Hopkin, 2005).

Enchytraeids are ecologically relevant species for soil toxicity. They can be used in laboratory tests as well as in field assays. Many enchytraeids are easy to handle and breed and the reproduction time (4-6 weeks) is less than for earthworms (8 weeks). Soil dwelling annelids of the genus *Enchytraeus* are used in toxicity tests. A reproduction test with *Enchytraeus albidus* has been standardized by OECD (2004b). This species has a worldwide distribution and it is found in marine freshwater and terrestrial habitats, mainly in decaying organic matter.

Tests with isopods are less developed. The species employed are *Porcellio scaber* and *Oniscus asellus* (Drobne and Hopkin, 1994; Van Brummelen et al., 1996). The main problem associated to the use of these species is their low growth rate and long reproductive cycle. They are widespread and act breaking down leaf material into smaller particles, which are more easily decomposed by microorganisms. The isopods tests measure the effects in feeding rates, mainly through feeding repellence.

Plants are an important taxonomic group to test soil quality. Different methods have been developed to study the toxicity of chemicals to plants. Phytotoxicity endpoints are measures of the survival or growth than can be reported as the change in height/length or biomass. Specific metabolic enzymes, total respiration and dark respiration have been also used as measures of endpoints. Sensitivity is highly dependent on plant species. Consequently, the use of several test species, widely distributed within plants taxonomy, is advisable to provide better information on effects in the environment. A list of recommended species for testing may be viewed in (OECD, 2006a). The chemical bioconcentration is usually measured in plants because they act as an exposure path to animals (including humans) through the food chain.

The microbial test consists in measuring effects on their functions, while structural (species oriented) testing is considered of lower relevance. Microorganisms play a fundamental role in the soil ecosystem processes, such as decomposition of soil organic matter and the cycling of nutrient. However, due to functional redundancy, sensitive species can be replaced and the diversity can be altered without a significant effect on the functions. A great number of methods to determine the microbial function and activity have been developed. Two soil microorganism tests have been standardized by OECD (2000a, b): nitrogen and carbon transformation. These tests measure soil respiration and N mineralization which are important processes in the carbon and nitrogen cycles, respectively. In addition, assays are available for a large number of soil enzymes, including dehydrogenases, $\beta$-glucosidases, ureases, amidases, phosphatases, arylsulfatases, cellulases and phenol oxidases (Dick et al., 1996).

Aquatic toxicity tests have achieved a higher development than testing protocols for soil organisms. The main exposure route is direct uptake from water (waterborne exposure) although uptake can also occur from food. One limitation to perform aquatic toxicity tests with leachates is the necessity of using static systems. The concentration of the chemical in the water can change due to adsorption and metabolism by the test organism and volatilization or degradation processes and sorption to particles. However, this allows determining effects due to the actual exposure and consequently, assays, if well designed, can be more representative for the expected exposure in the field. Aquatic toxicity is mainly evaluated using fish, daphnids, green algae and vascular plants. Fish, daphnids and algae are required in the risk assessment of chemical substances.

Fish are key organisms in the assessment of waters due to their diversity, their importance in natural ecosystems and their economical value. Moreover, they play an important role as they are secondary consumers. Consequently, fish bioaccumulation is frequently measured in relation to human exposure trough food. Different fish tests have been standardized by OECD (1984b;1992b,c;1998b;2000c). In these assays different species and different stages of the life cycle (eggs, embryo or adults) are employed. Lethal and sublethal effects (hatching, abnormal behaviour, malformations, etc) are assessed at different exposure times. Fish toxicity can be also assessed at the cellular level. The main advantage of *in vitro* assays using cell fish is that they reduce the use of vertebrates in toxicity studies and the volumes of leachates necessary to perform the tests. Moreover, they show a fast response and are usually simple to perform and analyze. However, a bigger effort is necessary to relate effects at the sub-organism level to effects at higher organizational levels and hence to ecosystem effects.

Invertebrates occupy a key position as primary consumers in the aquatic food chain. The toxicity to this taxonomic group has mostly been based on the cladoceran crustacean, *Daphnia*. The selection of daphnids is due to their broad distribution in fresh water bodies, their role in the food chain and the ease of handling in the laboratory. Most of the protocols recommend *Daphnia magna* o *Daphnia pulex* as test substance. An acute and a chronic test have been standardized by OECD (1998a; 2004c), using immobilization and reproductively as endpoints, respectively. A related genus, *Ceriodaphnia*, with a shorter life-span, is frequently used in North America for cost/effective chronic testing.

In algae tests, the effects on growth are determined on a green algal population growing exponentially in an enriched medium (e.g. ASTM, 1990; OECD, 2006b). The algal growth test is a chronic test since growth rate is rapid and effects can be assessed over several generations. Cell concentrations are measured using an electronic particle counter, a microscope with a counter chamber, a fluorimeter, a spectrophotometer, etc. The most frequent species used are unicellular green algae of rapid growth such as *Pseudokirchneriella subcapitata, Desmodesmus subspicatus* and *Chlorella vulgaris*. Ease of culture, visibility and availability are some of the criteria used to select these algal species.

Vascular plants and macrophytes are important in the functioning of freshwater ecosystems. The duckweeds (Family Lemnaceae) are widely distributed throughout the world. *Lemma gibba* and *Lemna minor* have been the most extensive studied species. They are easy to culture and have a rapid reproductive rate. Standardize methods have been published by different associations (e.g. ASTM, 2003; OECD, 2006c). The test endpoint is inhibition of growth and the measurement variable is frond number. Although results of *Lemna* are used in regulatory processes, algae continue being the predominant test species in aquatic phytotoxicity tests.

Finally, two bacterial toxicity tests have been often used to analyze the toxicity of waste and soil leachates. The bioluminescence assay with *Vibrio fischeri* (ISO, 1998) is probably the most widely used. This luminescent marine bacterium is sensible to a wide range of heavy metal chlorides and narcotics (Johnson et al., 1942). Because of the fast metabolism of this bacterial cell, this assay is much faster than other comparable assays and allows a rapid measure of the leachate toxicity. In this test, the addition of contaminants modifies the light emission, which is measured in a photometer after a given interval. The test is sensible, reproducible and precise. However, its relevance has been largely discussed mainly due to the use of a marine bacterial. Soil leachates have been also tested to mutagenicity using *Salmonella typhimurium* strain (Ames et al., 1975). However, the ecological relevance of mutagenicity test results for soils is difficult to evaluate.

## 4.3. BATTERY OF SINGLE SPECIES ASSAYS

Differences in species sensitivity to different contaminants, stress that a valid assessment of the environmental hazard of contaminated soils can only be obtained on the basis of test covering different key organisms. Soil quality assessment can be performed using a battery of single-species assays on soil organisms and aquatic organisms conducted on the leachates (Van Gestel et al., 2001; Robidoux et al., 2004b). Tests developed for the toxicity analyses of chemicals may be used to test environmental samples without excessive protocol changes. A selection of tests that may be employed for the investigation of soil pollution is given in table 1. The selection of the appropriate test organisms to measure soil toxicity is complicated. The approach usually consists in defining a simplified hypothetical ecosystem including organisms which belong to different trophic levels, with different feeding and different phylogenetic characteristics. In leachate assessments, the selected organisms usually include algae as primary producers, aquatic invertebrates as primary consumers and fish as secondary consumers. In soil assessments, the organisms belonging to three taxonomic groups are included, plants as producers, terrestrial invertebrates as consumers and microorganisms as decomposers.

The tests can also be selected depending on the use of the soil, the soil functions and the entities to be protected. Dott et al. (1995) proposed a stepwise approach for the assessment of the ecotoxic potential of soils with different land uses and soil functions.

## 4.4. MICROCOSMS

An alternative to a battery of independent toxicity tests is the use of multispecies systems in microcosms. This method allows assessing at the same time toxicity to several interacting organisms being exposed simultaneously. The method assumes that interactions between species can make a system more sensitive and/or realistic when assessing the effects of contaminants than that expected according to single species toxicity. Moreover, microcosm tests may incorporate and contribute to determine the environmental fate and behavior of contaminants in the soil.

Usually the system consists in a column of soil with a device to collect the leachate from below. Water is applied at regular times and it is collected using a funnel. Water addition simulates rainwater percolating through the soil. Two types of microcosms have been often used: intact soil cores with autochthonous soil organisms (US EPA, 1996; Sheppard, 1997; Knacker et al., 2004) and artificial assemblages adding soil organisms on sieved soil columns (Salminen and Haimi, 1997; Chen and Edwards, 2001; Fernández et al. 2004). Both systems have been developed to test potentially harmful substances.

The application of the first approach to the assessment of contaminated soils is difficult. Intact soil cores with naturally occurring organisms allow analyzing effects to the indigenous biota under defined laboratory conditions. However, these organisms have been exposed to, and selected by the toxicants for long periods and consequently the development of resistance to exposed contaminants and the selection of the less sensitive species is expected (Loibner et al., 2003). In this case, the effects studied are limited to the ecosystem functions such as soil respiration or nitrification capacity. For ecotoxicological testing of soil quality, the latter approach seems to be more appropriate. It allows determining toxicity to a set of selected organisms not previously exposed to contaminants. Moreover, experimental variations between replicates units are minimized (van Straalen and van Gestel, 1993). It is also possible to adapt these types of soil microcosms to the conditions required to test contaminated soils, the MS·3 approach developed at INIA and presented later on in this chapter represents a good example.

## 4.5. DATA INTERPRETATION

### 4.5.1. Statistical Analyses

Two different types of statistical analyses are possible depending on the experimental design. In the first, the experimental conditions comprise a control plus a number of concentrations replicated a number of times. The aim is to obtain a quantitative concentration-response relationship by regression analyses. In the second a non-diluted sample is assessed, and the effects on contaminated soil are compared to a reference or control soil.

In the first case, the data may be fit to a linear regression by performing a transformation of response data for instance using a logit-probit (Litchfield and Wilcoxon) or Weibull units (Christensen and Nyholm, 1984). Through a process known as inverse estimation, a concentration corresponding to a specified percentage effect relative to the control is estimated. As a difference with the analyses of chemical substances, data are referred as dilution of contaminated soil instead of concentration (i.e. the dilution of tested soil corresponding to a given percentage of effect is estimated). Confidence intervals can be calculated and hence, the precision of L(E)Cx obtained may be determined. These methods are appropriate to use on quantal data (e.g. mortality). For continuous data (e.g. growth) other methods are more appropriate (OECD, 2005).

In the second method, the test soil and the control soil are compared using analysis of variance (ANOVA). A disadvantage of testing only a soil concentration is that if experimental variability is relatively high, the sensitivity of the analyses to detect differences from control will be relatively low. This implies that only large differences from the control can be detected. The sensitivity of statistical analyses can be improved, increasing the number of replicates. The detection of no effect for toxic samples (false negative results) can be also due to insufficient sensitivity of the test method. This is especially important in the assessment of remediation processes where the levels of the contaminants have been reduced. It is a limitation of the use of bioassays since they allow detecting toxicity effects in polluted soils but not always in remediated soils.

## 4.6. HAZARD SOIL CLASSIFICATION

Bioassays may be applied for screening purposes to identify toxic samples. In this case, a simple differentiation of test results using toxic or not toxic is sufficient. However, this qualitative approach is not sufficient to quantify the risk potential of contaminated soils (Maxam et al., 2000). To incorporate direct toxicity assays in regulatory frameworks, toxicity classification systems which allow attributing a hazard score to polluted samples in accordance with increasing levels of toxicity are desirable. Thus, the evaluation of the results should be made with the help of threshold values, similar to the threshold values used in the fields of the chemical analyses.

Different methods have been proposed for ranging toxicity in assays performed with complex samples. However, none of the classification methods so far has fond general acceptance at the international level. Most of them are based on batteries of short-term toxicity tests, performed on dilution series of original samples. Some methods are based in the value of Toxic Units (TU), described as the inverse of the L(E)C50 expressed in % (Sprague and Ramsay, 1965). This expression is the dilution factor, which must be applied to the sample to obtain a 50% effect. Different categories of soil toxicity are established according to the TU value determined. These categories range from non toxic (TU<1) until extremely toxic (TU>100) (Bulich, 1982). This method has been widely applied to waste waters and waste leachates classification (Clément et al. 1996; Persoone et al., 2003).

Another approach attributes soil to classes of hazard on the basis of the lowest ineffective dilution (LIDx), which is defined as the dilution at which the effect is below an established percentage (x). This method has been applied to aqueous soil extracts (Maxam et al., 2000; Hund-Rinke et al., 2002) which are considered toxic or not toxic using a different percentage depending on the test specie, ranging from 10 % (e.g. algae test) to 20 % (e.g. luminescence test). A classification of hazard for the sample is given on the basis of the LID obtained for the most sensitive test species by Selivanovskaya and Latypova (2003). Accordingly, threshold values of $LID_{10}$ are established allowing designed samples to four classes of hazard (hazardous to non-hazardous)

The "Chemical equivalent method" expresses L(E)C50 values as chemical equivalent, which mean the chemical concentration that would cause the same toxicity as the pollution in the soil. Soil toxicity is related to the content of potent reference compound. These compounds are selected according to soil contamination (Leitgib et al. 2007).

Complex index including toxicity responses, consideration of routes of exposure, level of response (acute lethal or chronic sublethal) and sensitivity of the assays can also ser defined (e.g. Bombardier and Berminghan, 1999, developed for sediments).

In the Spanish regulation, dilution values are defined, which, if exceeded, indicate a high ecotoxicological risk. The proposed criteria consider a high risk if the short-term L(E)C50 value for the most sensitive soil taxonomic group is lower than 10 mg sample soil /g total soil or if short term L(E)C50 values of soil leachates to the most sensitive specie of aquatic organisms is lower than 10 ml leachate /l solution. This is equivalent to a limit of 100 TUs described above. On the other hand, potential risk exists if toxicity in one test performed with non-diluted samples indicates toxicity.

Threshold values can also be based on percentages of toxicity. For example, Phillips et al. (2001) established a threshold based in the difference in organism response between the sample and control. This threshold is established as a percentile of minimum significant difference value. Value of percentile is specific to each toxicity test.

In all the approaches mentioned above to classify soils the last step consists in deciding which level of soil toxicity is acceptable. This decision should be based in the potential risk to the ecosystem. With this aim, the probability that the effects measured in the laboratory will occur in the field, has to be quantified. Consequently, the development of models which allow predicting ecological effects from laboratory assays, is necessary. In summary, bioassays endpoints are quantitative measures of toxicity, which can be used to characterize contaminated soils and priories soils to remediation. However, before the extensive apply of bioassays to regulations, more information must be obtained as how the results of bioassays are related to the hazard classification of soil.

# Chapter 5

# SOIL CHARACTERIZATION USING MS-3: A CASE STUDY

Terrestrial microcosms are a powerful tool to study soil quality. These systems can be used to evaluate qualitatively the fate of chemicals, their effects on structural and functional aspects of ecosystems and to develop conceptual models of chemical transport, fate and effects (Gillett and Witt, 1979). In this section the application of a microcosm system denominated "Multispecies Soil System" (MS-3) for soil characterization is presented. This soil microcosm system was initially designed in the Laboratory for Ecotoxicology (INIA) to test pure chemicals and complex mixtures (Fernández et al., 2004; Boleas et al., 2005a, 2005b). However the usefulness of MS-3 for the characterization of polluted soils has been proved in different assays (Fernández et al., 2005).

The Multispecies Soil System (MS-3) consists of soil columns coupled to a leachate collector system. Representative soil macro-organisms (plants and terrestrial invertebrates) are introduced into these soil columns. These organisms, as well as the soil microbial community, are exposed to chemicals under simulated realistic environmental conditions. During the exposure period, the system is watered to simulate rainfall events, and artificial sunlight is provided for plant growth and to provide a photoperiod and temperature gradient approaching natural conditions. Leachates are collected and tested for toxicity using representative aquatic organisms (i.e. algae, daphnia and fish cell-lines) for which test procedures have been standardized.

In order to determine soil toxicity to soil organisms, after 21 days MS-3 columns are opened and the number of adult earthworms surviving as well as emergence of seedlings and aerial biomass production are recorded. The effects to microorganisms may be determined using the soil respiration test and nitrogen transformation test following the principles of standardized methods (OECD, 2000a; 200b) or by measurement of enzymatic activities: dehydrogenases and phosphatases (Boleas et al., 2005b). Toxicity of soil to aquatic organisms is determined for the leachate samples obtained from the soils in the microcosms using aquatic tests that included an algal test (OECD, 2006b; Ramos et al., 1996), the daphnid test (OECD, 2004c) and the RTG-2 fish cell line test (Babín et al., 2001), to measure growth, immobilization, and cytotoxicity of leachate respectively. Cytotoxicity is determined to RTG-2 fish cell line (ATCC, CL N° 55) using four different endpoints parameters: enzymatic activities as 7-ethoxyresorufin O-deethylase (EROD) (Bols et al., 1999) and β-Galactosidase (Pablos et al., 1998), uptake of neutral red stain (NR) to evaluate cell viability (Borenfreund and Puerner, 1985) and FRAME KB protein assay to evaluate cell detachment from a substrate (Knox et al., 1986).

The goal of the system was to develop a cost-effective system which provided useful information on both, adverse effects of pollutants on soil dwelling organisms and the capability of the pollutants to migrate through the soil matrix, providing an indication of their mobility and the possible risk to reach the aquatic compartment and produce adverse effects on aquatic organisms. Next, a practical example of the application of this approach for the assessment of polluted sites is presented. Five soils taken from different sites contaminated with organic and/or inorganic substances were assessed using the MS-3 microcosm system. The main physicochemical characteristic of these soils were shown in table 2. Chemical characterization of soils was based on the historical use of the site. All soils were contaminated with metals at different concentrations. Soil 1 showed the highest metal concentrations. Soil 2 and soil 5 were also contaminated with organic substances. Soil 2 presented levels of polychlorinated byphenyls (PCB) and hexachlorocyclohexanes (HCH). Soil 5 contained also concentrations of petroleum hydrocarbons. Procedures for soil toxicity assessment using MS-3 were accomplished as described by Fernández et al. (2005).

Two approaches were used to direct toxicity assessment of contaminated soils. In the former one, soils were tested in non diluted samples and toxicity data were obtained as percentage of inhibition compared to the control soil. Toxicity responses obtained in test soils were compared with those in the control soil by one-way analysis of variance (ANOVA), with Fisher's least significant difference procedure (LSD, $P< 0.05$). In the second approach soils were tested at four dilutions of contaminated soil: 6.25, 12.5, 25 and 50 % (w/w) for subsequent calculation of L(E)C50 using probit analyses.

# Table 2. Main physicochemical characteristics and soil chemical concentrations in the control and test soils

| | Texture | | | pH w (1-2.5) | Organic matter % | Metals mg/kg | | | | | PCB µg/kg | HCH µg/kg | TPH mg/kg |
|---|---|---|---|---|---|---|---|---|---|---|---|---|---|
| | Clay % | Silt % | Sand % | | | As | Cd | Cu | Pb | Zn | | | |
| Control Soil | 7.8 | 18.8 | 73.4 | 7.27 | 1.9 | nm | 0.2 | 27 | 31.3 | 62 | nm | nm | nd |
| Soil 1 | 17.4 | 19.7 | 62.9 | 5.56 | 17.5 | 2492 | 209 | 13547 | 24127 | 7458 | nm | nm | nm |
| Soil 2 | 12.3 | 29.4 | 58.3 | 6.9 | 10.3 | 484 | 44 | 372 | 4084 | 1056 | 189 | 43 | nm |
| Soil 3 | 5.15 | nm | nm | 7.9 | 1.1 | nm | 9.6 | 67 | 480 | 5900 | nm | nm | nm |
| Soil 4 | 25.6 | nm | nm | 6.3 | 4.6 | nm | 9.2 | nm | 431 | 1254 | nm | nm | nm |
| Soil 5 | 15.5 | 43.8 | 40.7 | 7.82 | 3.8 | 68 | 1.6 | 600 | 986 | 1476 | 98 | 199 | 974 |

Note. nm: not measured; nd: not detected.

Toxicity data to soil organisms obtained in the assessment of non diluted samples of soils using the MS-3 microcosm system are shown in table 3. Soils were assessed at 100 % soil concentration except in the carbon mineralization test, where soils were tested at 10 % (w/w) concentration of contaminated soil, to minimize interferences in the test due to differences in microbial biomass between control and test soils. In contaminated soils, an active microbial population may exist as a consequence of the adaptation of soil microbial populations to the contaminants (Bruins et al., 2000). Assessment of diluted soils allows testing the effects of contaminated soils to non-adapted populations of the control soil.

As expected, the toxic effects varied substantially depending on soil and test species. All soils were toxic to plants. However, effects varied with the plant specie tested and the endpoint measured (emergence of seedling or growth). Effects to earthworms were observed only for soil 1 and soil 3. Inhibition of carbon mineralization was observed with soil 3, soil 4 and soil 5. The lowest percentages of inhibition were observed in the carbon mineralization test, however, these do not indicate a lower sensitivity of microorganisms to these soils since in this test, soils were assessed at a lower concentration (10% soil concentration).

Soil 1 presented high effect on earthworm survival with 100 % of mortality. In the plant test statistical analyses revealed significant differences on wet mass of shoots between treatment and control soil to three species tested, but not on seedling emergence. Wet weight was significantly reduced with respect to control soil in *T. aestivum* (52 ± 9 %), *B. napus* (81 ± 20%) and *T. pratense* (51 ± 11 %). No inhibition of carbon mineralization was observed for soil 1, indicating that the microbial communities were not adversely affected in this soil.

Soil 2 was the least toxic presenting toxicity only for one among the eight endpoints measured. A decrease on *T. pratense* weight equal to 47±9 % was the only adverse effect observed. Earthworms and microorganisms were not affected.

Soil 3 produced toxic effect to all taxonomic groups tested. This soil caused a 25±1 % of earthworm mortality. In the plant assay, soil 3 adversely affected seedling emergence and plant growth for *T. aestivum*, with values equal to 72±10 % and 48±5 %, respectively. Microorganisms were also adversely affected with 32±1 % inhibition of carbon mineralization.

Soil 4 was toxic to plants and microorganisms. In the plant test, wet weight was significantly reduced with respect to control soil only in *T. aestivum* growth (44 ± 7 %) whereas a decrease of seedling emergence was observed in B. *napus* (68 ± 6 %). Soil 4 produced a slight (9.9 ± 0.2%) but significant inhibition of carbon mineralization.

Soil 5 presented toxicity to plants and microorganisms. This soil did not adversely affect earthworm survival. A significant decrease of seedling emergence compared to the control soil was observed in *T. aestivum* (85±8 %) and T. *pratense* (65±11 %), whereas growth was not affected in any of plant species tested. An significant inhibition of carbon mineralization of 14 ± 1 % was observed.

A high toxicity should be expected for these soils according to soil metal contents. However, toxicity was lower than the expected from total metal concentrations, suggesting a low bioavailability of metals in this soil. In all soils, the soil lead level (431-24127 mg kg$^{-1}$ soil dry wt) was higher than the data of L(E)C50 values described in the literature (ECOTOX Database) for plants (EC50=50-100 mg kg$^{-1}$ soil dry wt) and for earthworm (EC50=3.7-10 mg kg$^{-1}$ soil dry wt). However only adverse effects to earthworm survival were observed with soil 1 and soil 3. Moreover, effects in soil 3 were 25 ± 1 % of mortality despite that the lead level in this soil was 480 mg kg$^{-1}$ soil dry wt. Likewise, soil 2 with high contain in lead and other metals did not present toxicity to any soil organisms tested except a decrease of *T. pratense* weight (47 ± 9 %). This seems to indicate that the contaminants in this soil are not biologically available. Total concentrations can overestimate the real risk, as aging processes can strongly reduce the bioavailability, and, subsequently, the toxicity of pollutants (Song et al., 2006; Oorts et al., 2007). Consequently, it is difficult to estimate the potential risk of a soil contaminated by a complex mixture of substances attending exclusively to chemical characterization. Direct toxicity assays complement soil characterization based in chemical analyses since they allow direct assessment of the bioavailable fraction of the soil contaminants as well as synergistic and antagonistic interactions.

Bioassays were also performed on dilution series of the original samples of soil 3 and soil 5. A dose response relation was observed for some of the endpoints measured and L(E)C50 was determined (table 4). Ecotoxicity of aqueous leachates obtained from soil 3 and soil 5 was tested to algae, daphnia and fish. Toxicity of leachates to aquatic organism indicates transfer of contaminants from soil to leachates and the potential risk of soil to surface and ground waters. In soil 3, a dose-response relation with percentages of effects higher than 50 % was observed only for growth of *B. napus* and carbon mineralization. For soil 5, L(E)C50 could be estimated for soil organisms including the three taxonomic groups and for one aquatic organism (algae) exposed to the leachates of this soil.

# Table 3. Toxicity data to soil organisms exposed to non diluted samples of soils 1, 2, 3, 4, 5 and 6, respectively, in the microcosm system MS-3

| | Percentage of inhibition compared with control soil (%) | | | | | | | |
| | Earthworms* | Plants | | | | | | Microorganisms** |
| | | Triticum aestivum | | Brassica napus | | Trifolium pratense | | |
| | Mortality | Seedling Emergence | Wet weight plant | Seedling Emergence | Wet weight plant | Seedling Emergence | Wet weight plant | C. Transformation |
|---|---|---|---|---|---|---|---|---|
| Soil 1 | $100\pm0^a$ | ns | $52\pm9^a$ | ns | $81\pm20$ | ns | $51\pm11^a$ | ns |
| Soil 2 | ns | ns | ns | ns | ns | ns | $47\pm9^a$ | ns |
| Soil 3 | $25\pm1^b$ | $72\pm10^a$ | $48\pm5^a$ | ns | ns | ns | ns | $32\pm1^a$ |
| Soil 4 | ns | ns | $44\pm7^a$ | $68\pm6$ | ns | ns | ns | $9.9\pm0.2^b$ |
| Soil 5 | ns | $85\pm8^a$ | ns | ns | ns | $65\pm11$ | ns | $14\pm1^b$ |

Note. Shown data were significantly different from control ($P<0.05$) by LSD procedure; ns: not significantly different from control. Different letters indicate significantly different values using one-way ANOVA (LSD; $P<0.05$);

* In earthworm, the percentage of mortality was determined in relation to the number of organisms in the test (10 organisms in each microcosm).

** Microorganisms toxicity was assessed at a concentration of 1.0 g test soil /10 g soil.

**Table 4. Toxicity data to soil organisms and aquatic organisms exposed to diluted samples of soils 3 and 5, in the microcosm system MS-3**

| Soil | Test organism | Endpoint | L(E)C50 % (w/w) soil concentration | TU | Description |
|------|---------------|----------|-----------------------------------|-----|-------------|
| Soil 3 | Plants (B. napus) | Wet weight plant | 48 (36-87) | 2.1 (2.8-1.2) | Acute Toxicity (1<TU<10) |
|      | Microorganisms | C. transformation | 50 (42-62) | 2.0 (2.4-1.6) | Acute Toxicity (1<TU<10) |
| Soil 5 | Earthworms | Mortality | 10 (2-15) | 10.0 (50.0-6.7) | High Acute Toxicity (10<TU< 50) |
|      | Plants (T. aestivum) | Seedling emergence | 21 (15-28) | 4.8 (6.7-3.6) | Acute Toxicity (1<TU<10) |
|      | Plants (T. pratense) | Seedling emergence | 18 (14-23) | 5.6 (7.1-4.3) | Acute Toxicity (1<TU<10) |
|      | Microorganisms | C. transformation | 30 (26-35) | 3.3 (3.8-2.9) | Acute Toxicity (1<TU<10) |
|      | Algae | Growth rate | 30 (23-40) | 3.3 (4.3-2.5) | Acute Toxicity (1<TU<10) |

Data are expressed as L(E)C50 values.

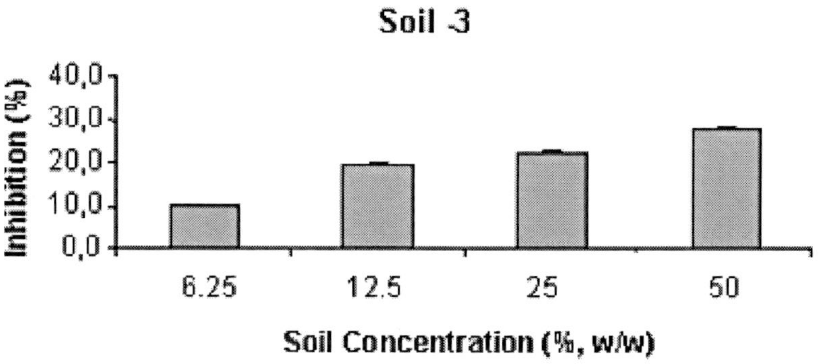

Figure 4. Inhibition growth rate of algae exposed to leachates from soil 3 determined according to OECD (2006b).

To soil organisms, soil 3 showed a concentration-dependent effect on *B. napus* growth and carbon mineralization with an EC50 = 48 (36-87) % and EC50 = 50 (42-62) % (w/w) soil concentration, respectively. To aquatic organisms, soil 3 produced a dose-response inhibition of algae growth rate, which was lower than 50% of effect at the highest concentration tested (figure 4). Effects were also observed to daphnia and fish, which cannot be explained from the soil concentration. In both organisms, the least effect was observed when these organisms were exposed to leachates obtained from soil at the highest concentration tested (50 %). In the daphnids test, significant differences were observed for *Daphnia magna* exposed to the leachates from control soil and soil 3 at 6.25, 12.5 and 25 % soil concentration (mean value = 51 ± 10 %), whereas leachates obtained from soil 50% did not cause any adverse effect. Likewise, EROD activity decreased at 6.25, 12.5 and 25 % (mean value = 54 ± 3 %) whereas at the highest concentration tested (50%, w/w, soil concentration) the lowest effect was measured (27 ± 3 %). Toxicity of leachates to aquatic organism depends, in part, on the nature of the contaminants as well as on the transfer of pollutants from soil to leachates. Changes in the physicochemical soil properties can affect the behaviour of contaminants in the soil. Dilution processes may release pollutants and this effect increases as high dilution factor increases. Differences observed at 50% soil concentration may be due to a lower availability of metals at this concentration.

Soil 5 produced a toxic effect greater than 50% on all soil taxonomic groups. A concentration-dependent effect on earthworm survival, carbon mineralization and seedling emergence of *T. aestivum* and *T. pratense* was observed. To aquatic organisms, leachates obtained from soil 5 adversely affected algae growth rate. The assay with RTG-2 cells indicated a toxic response only when EROD and β-galactosidase activity were measured. A decrease of EROD activity was observed at all concentrations tested, which a percentage of effect equal to 93 ± 12 % at the highest concentration tested (50 % soil concentration). However, EC50 cannot be estimated. Leachates from soil 5 caused inhibition of β-galactosidase activity (90±7 %) only at the highest dose tested (50% soil concentration).

It is interesting to compare toxicity data obtained in the assessment of soil 3 and 5 in both approaches: non diluted samples and dose-response assay. Differences of toxicity to earthworm obtained with the soil 5 in both assays are especially remarkable. Survival of earthworm was highly affect in the assay performed with diluted samples with a value of LC50=10 (2-15) (w/w) soil concentration. Conversely, the assay performed with non diluted samples of soil 5 did not show effect in earthworm survival. In addition, inhibition of *B. napus* growth was observed with soil 3 in the dose-response assay whereas the assay with non diluted soils did not affected this plant specie.

Differences observed between both approaches may be due to the differences in the method used to statistical analyses of data in both or to changes in the contaminant bioavailability in the soil affecting toxicity. The statistical analysis is different in both approaches. In the assay with non diluted samples the data obtained in the test soil are compared to the control using analysis of variance (ANOVA). If experimental variability is relatively high, then the sensitivity of the analyses to detect differences from control will be relatively low. This implies that only larger differences from the control can be detected and false negatives can be obtained. On the other hand, toxicity of contaminants in the soil may decrease with time due to adsorption and aging processes. However, some of these processes may be reversible by changes in physicochemical soil properties (Alexander, 2000). Contaminants may be released and become bioavailable. Moreover, these changes in the bioavailable fraction may be different for each specie and exposure route. In the bioassays with diluted samples, dilution processes can modify the bioavailability of chemicals in the soil, and hence their toxicity. In the earthworm assay with non diluted soil 5, the variation coefficient for the control and the test soil was 0%, which indicates that the lack of toxicity observed is not due to the analysis method. Consequently, toxicity observed in diluted samples seems due to pollutants released from soil as a consequence of dilution processes. A disadvantage of using diluted samples is that if the sample is not enough toxic, L(E)C50 cannot be determined. For example, in the assay with non diluted samples (100 % soil concentration), soil 3 affected *T. aestivum* growth (48±5 %). However, the EC50 value cannot be determined with the concentrations assessed since 50% of inhibition was not got in the dose response test.

Toxicity values may be used for ranking soils considering possible risk for the environment. With this end, toxicity data obtained for soil 3 and soil 5 were compared. In the assay with non diluted samples, soil 3 was toxic to all taxonomic groups tested whereas soil 5 did not affected earthworm survival. Levels of toxicity may be also compared in the different assays. Inhibition of carbon mineralization was significantly higher for soil 3 (32±1 %) than soil 5 (14±1 %). Regarding the plant test, the effects were different depending on the plant specie and the measured parameter. Both soils affect emergence of *T. aestivum* but no significant differences were observed between them. Soil 3 also affected growth of *T. aestivum* (48±5 %) whereas soil 5 showed significant effects on emergence of *T. pratense* (65±11 %). Comparison of results obtained in this assay for soil 3 and soil 5 seems to indicate increasing toxicity of soil 3 since this soil showed toxicity for a higher number of taxonomic groups and the higher toxicity observed in microorganisms.

In the second approach, soils are compared using a classification system, developed for wastes leachates (Persoone et al., 2003), based in the L(E)C50 values obtained for the different taxonomic groups. The L(E)C50 values are recalculated as Toxic Units, and cut-off values based in TU are established (table 4). According to this classification, the toxicity of soil 5 is higher than the toxicity of soil 3. Thus, soil 3 would be considered as toxic (1<TU<10) for all endpoint measured and soil 5 as highly toxic since L(E)C50 is reached in the 10-fold dilution (10<TU<100) for at least one test (earthworm mortality).

The Spanish legislation (Ministerio de Presidencia, 2005) includes assays with diluted and non diluted samples. Thus, a threshold to classify a soil as contaminated, based on the L(E)C50 values to soil and aquatic organisms is established. According to this criteria, if the short-term L(E)C50 value for the most sensitive soil taxonomic group is lower than 10 mg sample soil /g total soil or if short term L(E)C50 values of soil leachates to the most sensitive specie of aquatic organisms is lower than 10 ml leachate /l solution, the soil is declared contaminated. In addition, the lack of short-term toxicity in non diluted soil samples and leachates is essential to classify a soil as non-contaminated. Soil 3 and soil 5 toxic effects are observed below this threshold and consequently they cannot be declared as contaminated. However, as toxicity was observed with both soils for some taxonomic groups, the characterization of these soils requires further site-specific risk assessment.

The assay of soil at different concentrations to obtain a dose-response similar to chemical substances requires the analysis of a higher number of samples than the assay with non diluted samples. However, the information obtained in this work seems to indicate that the assessment of different concentrations provides additional information on the potential of soils to release contaminants to the environment due to physicochemical changes in the soil and the soil risk for spreading the contamination to other areas due to surface movement of contaminated soil caused by erosion, flooding, etc.

In summary, biological test and conventional chemical analyses of soils complement each other in the assessment of soil pollution. As showed in this study, risk analysis based in total soil concentration of chemicals can overestimate the real risk since the toxicity of metals in soils was less than that expected to correspond to metal soil concentration. The use of mutispecies laboratory terrestrial models to soil characterization allows making a more realistic approach for risk assessment. In the MS-3 system, the organisms were selected from different trophic levels and included taxonomic groups that cover essential ecological roles for the sustainability of soil use. The mobility, and possible risks for the aquatic compartment (groundwater and superficial water), can also be determined through a watering and subsequent leaching processes.

*Chapter 6*

# CONCLUSION

The assessment of soil quality regarding chemical pollution is complex, but a significant process has been achieved in recent years. Part of the complexity is related to the intricacy and variability of the relationships between the soil, as compartment, and its associated terrestrial community. Most species are not linked to the soil itself, but to the ground/above-ground interface. The main consequence is that the assessment must cover a multitude of exposure routes for receptors from different taxonomic groups. In addition, soil, as a complex matrix, has relevant physical-chemical interactions with the chemical pollutants, obviously, issues such as bioavailability and ageing are not exclusively observed for soil, but achieve particular relevance when assessing soil pollution. The main consequence is that is possible to set generic thresholds of potential concern, but they must be conservative for covering the differences in toxicity among soils for the same chemical. Thus, potential risk can be identified, but the confirmation of a real likelihood for ecological consequences requires additional considerations. The combination of chemical analysis and direct toxicity testing on the same soil sample offers a proper and cost/effective solution. Both, single-species tests and soil microcosms are nowadays available, offering the basis for a sound assessment of soil quality in relation to chemical pollution.

# REFERENCES

Adriano, DC. Trace elements in terrestrial environments. *Biogeochemistry, bioavailability and risk of metals.* 2nd Ed. New York: Springer-Verlag; 2001.

Aldenberg, T; Jaworska, JS; Traas, TP. Normal species sensitivity distributions and probabilistic ecological risk assessment. In: Posthuma L, Suter GW, Traas TP, editors. *The use of Species Sensitivity Distributions in ecotoxicology.* Boca Raton, FL, USA: Lewis Publishers; 2002; 49-102.

Alexander, M. Aging, bioavailability, and overestimation of risk from environmental pollutants. *Environmental Science and Technology,* 2000, 34, 4259-4265.

ASTM (American Society for Testing and Materials). Standard guide for conducting static 96h toxicity test with microalgae, E1218-90. Philadelphia: ASTM; 1990

ASTM (American Society for Testing and Materials). Standard guide for conducting static toxicity test with *Lemna gibba*, G3, E1415-91. Philadelphia: ASTM; 2003.

Ames , BN; McCann, J; Yamasaki, E. Methods for detecting carcinogens and mutagens with the Salmonella/mammalian-microsome mutagenicity test. *Mutation Research,* 1975, 31, 347–364.

Babín, MM; García, P; Fernández, C; Alonso, C; Carbonell, G; Tarazona JV. Toxicological characterization of sludge from sewage treatment plants using identification evaluation protocols based on in vitro toxicity tests. *Toxicology in vitro,* 2001, 15, 519-524.

Bols, NC; Schirmer, K; Joyce, ME; Dixon, DG; Greenberg, BM; Whyte, JJ. Ability of polycyclic aromatic hydrocarbons to induce 7-ethoxyrresorufin-o-deethylase activity in a trout liver cell line. *Ecotoxicology and Environmental Safety,* 1999, 44, 118-128.

BbodSchG (Bundes-Bodenschutzgesetz). *Gesetz zum Schutz des Bodens in der Fassung der Bekanntmachung vom* 17.03.1998. Bundesgesetzblatt I. 1998.

Beck, L; Römbke, J; Breure, AM; Mulder, C. Considerations for the use of soil ecological classification and assessment concepts in soil protection. *Ecotoxicology and Environmental Safety,* 2005, 62, 189-200

Bierkens, J; Klein, G; Corbisier, P; Van Den Heuvel, R; Verschaeve, L; Weltens, R; Schoeters, G. Comparative sensitivity of 20 bioassays for soil quality. *Chemosphere,* 1998, 37, 2935-2947.

Bispo, A; Jourdain, MJ; Jauzein, M. Toxicity and genotoxicity of industrial soils polluted by polycyclic aromatic hydrocarbons (PAHs). *Organic Geochemistry,* 1999, 30, 947-952.

Boleas, S; Alonso, C; Pro, J; Babín, MM; Fernández, C; Carbonell, G; Tarazona, JV. Effects of sulfachloropyridazine in MS-3 arable land: a multispecies soil system for assessing the environmental fate and effects of veterinary medicines. *Environmental Toxicology and Chemistry,* 2005a, 24, 811-819.

Boleas, S; Alonso, C; Pro, J; Fernández, C; Carbonell, G; Tarazona, JV. Toxicity of the antimicrobial oxytetracycline to soil organisms in a multispecies-soil system (MS-3) and influence of manure co-addition. *Journal of Hazardous Materials,* 2005b, 122, 233-241.

Bombardier, M; Bermingham, N. The SED-TOX index: Toxicity-directed management tool to assess and rank sediments based on their hazard. Concept and application. *Environmental Toxicology and Chemistry,* 1999, 18, 685-698.

Borenfreund, E; Puerner, JA. Toxicity determined in vitro by morphological alterations and neutral red absorption. Toxicology Letters, 1985, 24, 119-124.. Bruins, MR; Kapil, S; Oehme, FW. Microbial resistance to metals in the environment. *Ecotoxicology and Environmental Safety,* 2000, 45, 198-207.

Bulich, AA. A practical and reliable method for monitoring the toxicity of aquatic samples. Process Biochemistry, 1982, 17, 45-47.

Burton, GA Jr.; Batley, GE; Chapman, PM; Forbes, VE; Smith, EP; Reynoldson, T; Schlekat, CE; den Besten, PJ; Bailer, AJ; Green, AS; Dwyer, RL. A weight of evidence framework for assessing sediment (or other) contamination: improving certainty in the decision-making process. *Human and Ecological Risk Assessment,* 2002a, 8, 1675-1696.

Burton, GA Jr.; Chapman, PM; Smith, EP. Weight of evidence approaches for assessing ecosystem impairment. *Human and Ecological Risk Assessment,* 2002b, 8,1657-1673.

Cairns, J Jr. Quantification of biological integrity. In: Ballentine RK, Guarria LJ, editors. *Integrity of water.* Washington DC: USEPA Office of Water and Hazardous Materials; 1977; 171-187.

Calow, P. *Handbook of Ecotoxicology,* Vol 1. 1$^{st}$ Ed. Oxford: Blackwell Scientific Publications; 1993.

Campbell, PJ; Arnold, DJS; Brock, TCM; Grandy, NJ; Heger, W; Heinbach, F; Maund, S; Streloke, M. *Guidance document on higher tier aquatic risk assessment for pesticides* (HARAP). Brussels: SETAC-Europe; 1999.

Carlon, C; D'Alessandro, M; Swartjes, F. Derivation methods of soil screening values in Europe. A review and evaluation of national procedures towards harmonization. Report, EUR 22805 EN, 2007, European Chemical Bureau. *Ispra: Joint Research Centre y el Directorate General Environment de la Commission European;* 2007.

Clément, B; Persoone, G; Janssen, C; Le Dû-Delapierre, A. Estimation of the hazard of landfills through toxicity testing of leachates. *Chemosphere,* 1996, 33, 2303-2320.

Crommentuijn, T; Polder, MD; van de Plassche, EJ. Maximum permissible concentrations and negligible concentrations for metals, tacking background concentrations into account. *RIVM report N° 601501001;* 1997.

Crommentuijn, T; Polder, M; Sijm, D; de Bruijn, J; van de Plassche, E. Evaluation of the Dutch environmental risk limits for metals by application of the added risk approach. *Environmental Toxicology and Chemistry,* 2000, 19, 1692-1701.

Crossland, NO. Extrapolating from mesocosms to the real world. *Toxicology and Ecotoxicology News,* 1994, 1, 15-22.

CSTEE (Scientific Committee on Toxicity, Ecotoxicity and the Environment). CSTEE opinion on the available scientific approaches to assess the potential effects and risk of chemicals on terrestrial ecosystems. C2/JCD/esteeop/Ter91100/D(0), Brussels: *Reports of the Scientific Committee on Toxicity, Ecotoxicity and the Environment (CSTEE)* ; 2000, 178 pp.

Chen, SK; Edwards, CA. A microcosm approach to assess the effects of fungicides on soil ecological processes and plant growth: comparisons of two soil types. *Soil Biology and Biochemistry,* 2001, 33, 1981-1991.

Christensen, ER; Nyholm, N. Ecotoxicological assays with algae: Weibull dose–response curves. *Environmental Science and Technology,* 1984, 18, 713–718.

Dick, RP; Breakwell, DP; Turco, RF. Soil enzyme activities and biodiversity measurements as integrative microbiological indicators. In: Doran JW, Jones

AJ, editors. Methods for assessing soil quality. Madison, WI: *Soil Science Society of America;* 1996; 247-271

DIN 38414, Teil 4: Deutsche einheitsverfaheren zur Wasser-, Abwasser- und Schalammuntersuchung; Schalamm und Sediment (Gruppe S). Bestimmung der Eluierbarkeit mit Wasser (S4), 1984

Di Toro, DM; Allen, HE; Bergman, HL; Paquin, PR; Santore, RC. Biotic ligand model of the acute toxicity of metals. 1. *Technical basis. Environmental Toxicology and Chemistry,* 2001, 20, 2383-2396.

Dott, W; van Afferden, M; Ahlf, W; Crößmann, G; Daei, B; Dorgerloh, M; Eikmann, Th; Fabig, W; Gauglitz, U; van Gestel, CAM; Hartmann, A; Hund, K; Kästner, M; Kalnowski, G; Kanne, R; Müller-Wegener, U; Müller-Markgraf, W; Pfeifer, F; Rippen, G; Schäfer-Treffenfeld, W; Schulz-Berendt, V; Sellner, M; Sprenger, B; Weißenfels, WD; Werner, D; Wiegand-Rosinus, M; Wiesner, J; Wilke; BM. DECHEMA-Ad-hoc-committee Methods for toxicological/ecotoxicological assessment of soils; Frankfurt am Main, Germany: DECHEMA Deutsche Gesellschaft für Chemisches Apparatewesen, *Chemische Technik und Biotechnologie;* 1995.

Drobne, D; Hopkin, SP. Ecotoxicological laboratory test for assessing the effects of chemicals on terrestrial isopods. *Bulletin of Environmental Contamination and Toxicology,* 1994, 53, 390-397.

Ducrot, V; Pery, AR; Mons, R; Queau, H; Charles, S; Garric, J. Dynamic energy budget as a basis to model population-level effects of zinc-spiked sediments in the gastropod *Valvata piscinalis. Environmental Toxicology and Chemistry,* 2007, 26,1774-1783.

EC (European Commission). *Guidance document on aquatic ecotoxicology in the context of Directive* 91/414/EEC. SANCO /3268/2001 rev.4 (final). Brussels: European Commission; 2002a.

EC (European Commission). *Guidance document on terrestrial ecotoxicology in the context of Directive* 91/414/EEC. SANCO/10329/2002 rev.2(final). Brussels: European Commission; 2002b.

EC (European Commission). *Technical Guidance Documents in support of the Commission Directive 93/67/EEC on risk assessment for new notified substances and the Commission Regulation (EC) 1488/94 on risk assessment for existing substances.* Ispra: European Chemical Bureau; 2003.

Eom, IC; Rast, C; Veber, AM; Vasseur, P. Ecotoxicity of a polycyclic aromatic hydrocarbon (PAH)-contaminated soil. *Ecotoxicology and Environmental Safety,* 2007, 67, 190-205.

EU (European Union) Guidance Document on risk assessment for birds and mammals under Council Directive 91/414/EEC. SANCO/4145/2000,

*European Commission Health & Consumer Protection Directorate-General;* 2002; 44 pp.

EUFRAM. Concerted action to develop a European Framework for probabilistic risk assessment of the environmental impacts of pesticides. Introducing probabilistic methods into the ecological risk assessment of pesticides. *EUFRAM Report,* Vol. 1; 2006. http://www.eufram.com.

Ferguson, CC; Darmendrail, D; Freier K; Jensen, BK; Jensen, J; Kasamas, J; Urzelai, A; Vegter, J. *Risk Assessment For Contaminated Sites In Europe. Scientific Basis.* Vol. 1. Nottingham: LQM. Press; 1998.

Fernández, C; Alonso, C; Babín, MM; Pro, J; Carbonell, G; Tarazona, JV. Ecotoxicological assessment of doxycicline in aged pig manure using multispecies soil system. *Science of the Total Environment,* 2004, 323, 63-69.

Fernández, MD; Cagigal, E; Vega, MM; Urzelai, A; Babín, M; Pro, J; Tarazona, JV. Ecological risk assessment of contaminated soils through direct toxicity assessment. *Ecotoxicology and Environmental Safety,* 2005, 62, 174-184.

Fernández, MD; Vega, MM; Tarazona, JV. Risk-based ecological soil quality criteria for the characterization of contaminated soils. Combination of chemical and biological tools. *Science of the Total Environment,* 2006, 366, 466-484.

Forbes TL, Forbes VE. A critique of the use of distribution-based extrapolation models in ecotoxicology. *Functional Ecology,* 1993, 7, 249-254.

Fountain, MT; Hopkin, SP. Folsomia Candida (Collembola): An "standard" soil arthropod. *Annual Review of Entomology,* 2005, 50, 201-222.

Giddings, J; Brock, TCM; Heger, W; Heimbach, J; Maund, SJ; Norman, S; Ratte, HT; Schäfers, C; Streloke, M. Community level aquatic system studies. Interpretation citeria (CLASSIC). Pensacola FL, USA: *Society for Environmental Toxicology and Chemistry* (SETAC), 2002.

Greene, JC; Bartels, CL; Warren-Jicks, WJ; Parkhurst, BR; Linder, GL; Peterson, S; Miller, WE. Protocols for shot term toxicity screening of hazardous waste sites. OR, 600/3-88-029. *Corvallis: United States Environmental Protection Agency;* 1989; 102pp.

Hämmann, M; Gupta, SK; Zihler, J. Protection of soils from contamination in Swiss legislation. *Advances in GeoEcology,* 1998, 31, 629-636.

Hammel, W; Steubing, L; Debus, R. Assessment of ecotoxic potential of soil contaminants by using a soil-algae test. *Ecotoxicology and Environmental Safety,* 1998, 40, 173-176.

Holmgren, GGS; Meyer, MW; Chaney, RL; Daniels, RB. Cadmium, lead, zinc, cupper and niquel in agricultural soils of United States of America. *Journal of Environmental Quality,* 1993, 22, 335-348.

Hopkin, SP. *In situ* biological monitoring of pollution in terrestrial and aquatic ecosystems. In Calow P, editor. *Handbook of Ecotoxicology,* Vol 1. 1st Ed. Oxford: Blackwell Scientific Publications; 1993; 397-427.

Hund-Rinke, K; Kördel, W; Hennecke, D; Eisenträger, A; Heiden , S. Bioassays for the ecotoxicological and genotoxicological assessment of contaminated soils (Results of a Round Robin Test. *Journal of Soil and Sediments,* 2002, 2, 43-50.

Hund-Rinke, K; Kördel, W. Underlying issues in bioaccessibility and bioavailability: experimental methods. *Ecotoxicology and Environmental Safety,* 2003, 56, 52-62.

ISO (International Organization for Standardization). Water quality. Determination of the inhibitory effect of water samples on the light emission of Vibrio fischeri (Luminescent bacteria test). Part 1: *Method using freshly prepared bacteria.* No. ISO 11348-1:1998 ; Geneva: Int. Stand. Organ.; 1998; 16 pp.

ISO (International Organization for Standardization). *Soil quality-inhibition of reproduction of Collembolan (Folsomia candida) by soil pollutants.* No. ISO 11267:1999. Geneva: Int. Stand. Organ.; 1999; 16 pp.

Jager, DT; Vermeire, TG; Slooff, W; Roelfzema, H. Uniform system for the evaluation of substances. II Effects assessment. *Chemosphere,* 1994, 29, 319-335.

Janssen, RPT; Peijnenburg, WJGM; Posthuma, L; van den Hoop, MAGT. Equilibrium partitioning of heavy metals in Dutch field soils. II. Prediction of metal accumulation in earthworms. *Environmental Toxicology and Chemistry,* 1997,16, 2479-2488.

Johnson, FH; Caruer, CM; Harryman, WK. Luminous bacterial auxanograms in relation to heavy metals and narcotics, self-photographed in color. *Journal of Bacteriology,* 1942, 44, 703-713.

Keddy, CJ; Greene, JC; Bonnell, MA. Review of whole-organism bioassays: soil, freshwater sediment, and freshwater assessment in Canada. *Ecotoxicology and Environmental Safety,* 1995, 30, 221-251

Klein, M. PELMO: *Pesticide Leaching Model. Fraunhofer: Institut für Umweltchemie und Ökotoxicogie,* D57392 Schmallenberg; 1991.

Knacker, T; van Gestel, CAM; Jones, SE; Soares, AMVM; Schallnaβ, H-J; Förster, B; Edwards, CA. Ring-testing and field-validation of a Terrestrial Model Ecosystem (TME). An instrument for testing potentially harmful substances: conceptual approach and study design. *Ecotoxicology,* 2004, 13, 9-27.

Knox, P; Uphill, PF; Fry, JR; Beuford, J; Balls, M. The FRAME multicentre project on *in vitro* cytotoxicology. *Food Chemical Toxicology,* 1986, 24, 457-463.

Koster, M; de Groot, A; Vijver, M; Peijnenburg, W. Copper in the terrestrial environment: Verification of a laboratory-derived terrestrial biotic ligand model to predict earthworm mortality with toxicity observed in field soils. *Soil Biology and Biochemistry,* 2006, 38, 1788-1796.

Leistra, M; van der Linden, AMA; Bvoesten, JJTI; Tiktak, A; van den Berg, F. PEARL model for pesticide behaviour and emissions in soil-plant systems. *Description of processes.* Alterra report 13, RIVM report 711401009; 2000.

Leitgib, L; Kàlmàn, J; Gruiz, K. Comparison of bioassays by testing whole soil and their water extract from contaminated sites. *Chemosphere*, 2007, 66,428-434.

Lewis, HM; Law, R. Effects of dynamics on ecological networks. Journal of Theoretical Biology, 2007, 247, 64-76.

Litchfield, JT; Wilcoxon, F. A simplified method of evaluating dose effect experiments. *Journal of Pharmacology and Experimental Therapeutics,* 1949, 96, 99-113.

Lock, K; Janssen, CR. Ecotoxicity of zinc in spiked artificial soils versus contaminated field soils. *Environmental Science and Technology,* 2001, 35, 4295-4300.

Lock, K; Janssen, CR. Comparative toxicity of a zinc salt, zinc powder and zinc oxide to Eisenia fetida, *Enchytraeids albidus and Folsomia candida. Chemosphere,* 2003a, 53, 851-856.

Lock, K; Janssen, CR. Influence of ageing on zinc bioavailability in soils. *Environmental Pollution,* 2003b, 126, 371-374.

Loibner, AP; Szolar, OHJ; Braun, R; Hirmann, D. Ecological assessment and toxicity screening in contaminated land analysis. In: Thompson KC, Nathanail CP, editors. *Chemical analysis of contaminated land.* Oxford, UK: Blackwell Publishing Ltd; 2003; 229-267.

Long, ER; Chapman, PM. A sediment quality triad: measures of sediment contamination, toxicity and infaunal community composition in Puget Sound. *Marine Pollution Bulletin,* 1985, 16, 405-415.

Ma, Y; Lombi, E; Nolan, AL; McLaughlin, MJ. Short term natural attenuation of copper in soils: effects of time temperature and soil characteristics. *Environmental Toxicology and Chemistry,* 2005, 25, 652-658.

Maxam, G; Rila, JP; Dott, W; Eisentraeger, A. Use of bioassays for assessment of water-extractable ecotoxic potential of soils. *Ecotoxicology and Environmental Safety,* 2000, 45, 240-246.

McLaughlin, MJ; Hamon, RE; McLaren, RG; Speir, TW; Rogers, SL. Review: A bioavailability-based rationale for controlling metal and metalloid contamination of agricultural land in Australia and New Zealand. *Australian Journal of Soil Research,* 2000a, 38, 1037-1086.

McLaughlin, MJ; Zarcinas, BA; Stevens, DP; Cook, N. Soil testing for heavy metals. *Communications in Soil Science and Plant Analysis,* 2000b, 31, 1661-1700

Mendonca, E; Picado, A. Ecotoxicological monitoring of remediation in a coke oven soil. Environmental Toxicology, 2002, 17, 74-79.

Ministerio de Presidencia. REAL DECRETO 9/2005, de 14 de enero, por el que se establece la relación de actividades potencialmente contaminantes del suelo y los criterios y estándares para la declaración de suelos contaminados. *España: Boletín Oficial del Estado* 15/2005; 2005; 1833-1843.

NRC (National Research Council). *Issues in Risk Assessment.* Washington DC: National Academy Press; 1983; 374 pp.

OECD (Organization for Economic Cooperation and Development). *Guidelines for Testing of Chemicals.* Earthworm, acute toxicity tests. Test guideline N° 207. Paris, France; 1984a

OECD (Organization for Economic Cooperation and Development). Guidelines for Testing of Chemicals. Fish, Prolonged toxicity test:14-day study. *Test guideline N° 204.* Paris, France; 1984b.

OECD (Organization for Economic Cooperation and Development). Report of the OECD workshop on the extrapolation of laboratory aquatic toxicity data to the real environment. *OECD Environment Monograph 59,* OECD/GD (92)169. Paris, France; 1992a.

OECD (Organization for Economic Cooperation and Development). Guidelines for Testing of Chemicals. Fish, Acute toxicity test . *Test guideline N° 203.* Paris, France; 1992b.

OECD (Organization for Economic Cooperation and Development). Guidelines for Testing of Chemicals. Fish, early-life stage toxicity test. *Test guideline N° 210.* Paris, France; 1992c

OECD (Organization for Economic Cooperation and Development). Guidelines for Testing of Chemicals. Daphnia magna, reproduction test. *Test guideline N° 211.* Paris, France; 1998a

OECD (Organization for Economic Cooperation and Development). Guidelines for Testing of Chemicals. Fish, short-term toxicity test on embryo and sac-fry stages. *Test guideline N° 212.* Paris, France; 1998b

OECD (Organization for Economic Cooperation and Development). Guidelines for Testing of Chemicals. Soil micro-organisms, nitrogen transformation test. *Test guideline N° 217.* Paris, France; 2000a.

OECD (Organization for Economic Cooperation and Development). Guidelines for Testing of Chemicals. Soil micro-organisms, carbon transformation test. *Test guideline N° 217.* Paris, France; 2000b.

OECD (Organization for Economic Cooperation and Development). Guidelines for Testing of Chemicals. Fish, juvenile growth test. *Test guideline N° 215.* Paris, France; 2000c.

OECD (Organization for Economic Cooperation and Development). Guidelines for Testing of Chemicals. Earthworm reproduction test. *Test guideline N° 222.* Paris, France; 2004a.

OECD (Organization for Economic Cooperation and Development). Guidelines for Testing of Chemicals. Enchytraeid reproduction test. *Test guideline N° 220.* Paris, France. 2004b.

OECD (Organization for Economic Cooperation and Development). Guidelines for Testing of Chemicals. Daphnia s.p., acute immobilisation test. *Test guideline N° 202.* Paris, France; 2004c

OECD (Organization for Economic Cooperation and Development). Guidelines for Testing of Chemicals. Leaching in Soil Columns. *Test guideline N° 312.* Paris, France; 2004d.

OECD (Organization for Economic Cooperation and Development). *Current approaches in the statistical analyses of ecotoxicity data: a guidance to application.* Paris, France; 2005.

OECD (Organization for Economic Cooperation and Development). Guidelines for Testing of Chemicals. Terrestrial plants, growth test. *Test guideline N° 208.* Paris, France; 2006a

OECD (Organization for Economic Cooperation and Development). Guidelines for Testing of Chemicals. Alga, growth inhibition test. *Test guideline N° 201.* Paris, France; 2006b

OECD (Organization for Economic Cooperation and Development). Guidelines for Testing of Chemicals. Lemna s.p. Growth inhibition test. *Test guideline N° 221.* Paris, France; 2006c

Oorts, K; Ghesquiere, U; Smolders, E. Leaching and aging decrease nickel toxicity to soil microbial processes in soils freshly spiked with nickel chloride. *Environmental Toxicology and Chemistry,* 2007, 26, 1130-1138.

Pablos, MV; Boleas, S; García, P; Carbonell, G; Tarazona, JV. Inhibición de la actividad B-GAL como parámetro de toxicidad subletal interespecífico. *Cuadernos de Investigación Biológica,* 1998, 20, 471-474.

Parker, DR; Pedler, JF. Reevaluating the free-ion activity model of trace metal availability to higher plants. *Plant and Soil,* 1997, 196, 223-228.

Parkhurst, DL; Appelo, CAJ. User's guide to PHREEQC. A computer program for speciation, batch-reaction, one-dimensional transport and inverse geochemical calculations. *U.S. Geological survey water-resources investigations Report 99-4259*; 1999.

Peijnenburg, WJGM; Posthuma, L; Eijsackers, HJP; Allen, HE. A conceptual framework for implementation of bioavailability of metals for environmental management purposes. *Ecotoxicology and Environmental Safety,* 1997, 37, 163-172.

Persoone, G; Marsalek, B; Blinova, I; Torokne, A; Zarina, D; Manusadzianas, L; Nalecz-Jawecki, G; Tofan, L; Stepanova, N; Tothova, L; Kolar, B. A practical and user-friendly toxicity classification system with microbiotests for natural waters and wastewaters. *Environmental toxicology,* 2003, 18, 395-402.

Peterson, SA; Greene, JC; Miller, WE. Toxicological assessment of hazardous waste samples extracted with deionised water or sodium acetate (TCLP) leaching media. In: Friedman D, editors. Waste testing and quality assurance. Vol 2 ASTM STP 1062. Philadelphia, USA*: American Society for Testing and Materials;* 1990; 107-129.

Phillips, BM; Hunt, JW; Anderson, BS; Puckett, HM; Fairey, R; Wilson, CJ; Tjeerdema, R. Statistical significance of sediment toxicity test results: Threshold values derived by the detectable significance approach. *Environmental Toxicology and Chemistry,* 2001, 20, 371-373.

Posthuma, L; Suter, GW; Traas, TP. *The use of Species Sensitivity Distributions in ecotoxicology.* Boca Raton, FL, USA: Lewis Publishers; 2002.

Pugh, DM; Tarazona, JV. Environment & Policy. Vol 15. *Regulation for chemical safety in Europe: analysis, comment and criticism.* Dordrecht, The Netherlands: Kluwer Academic Publishers; 1998; 194 pp.

Ramade, F. Précis d'écotoxicologie. *Collection d'écologie 22.* Masson, Paris; 1992; pp 293.

Ramos, C; de la Torre, AI; Tarazona, JV; Muñoz, MJ. Desarrollo de un ensayo de inhibición de Chlorella vulgaris utilizando un test en microplacas. *Revista de Toxicología,* 1996, 13, 97-100.

Rand, GM. *Fundamentals of Aquatic Toxicology.* Washington, DC, USA: Taylor & Francis; 1995.

Robidoux, PY; Dubois C; Hawari J; Sunahara GI. Assessment of soil toxicity from an antitank firing range using Lumbricus terrestris and Eisenia andrei in mesocosms and laboratory studies. *Ecotoxicology,* 2004a, 13, 603-14.

Robidoux, PY; Gong, P; Sarrazin, M; Bardai, G; Paquet, L; Hawari, J; Dubois, C; Sunahara, GI. Toxicity assessment of contaminated soils from an antitank firing range. *Ecotoxicology and Environmental Safety,* 2004b, 58, 300-313.

Robidoux, PY; Svendsen, C; Sarrazin, M; Thiboutot, S; Ampleman, G; Hawari J; Weeks, JM; Sunahara, GI. Assessment of a 2,4,6-trinitrotoluene-contaminated site using Aporrectodea rosea and Eisenia andrei in mesocosms. *Archives of Environmental Contamination and Toxicology,* 2005, 48, 56-67.

Römbke, J; Breure, AM; Mulder, C; Rutgers, M. Legislation and ecological quality assessment of soil: implementation of ecological indication systems in Europe. *Ecotoxicology and Environmental Safety,* 2005, 62, 201-210.

Romijn, CAFM; Luttik, R; Canton, JH. Presentation of a general algorithm to include effect assessment on secondary poisoning in the derivation of environmental quality criteria. Terrestrial food chains. *Ecotoxicology and Environmental Safety,* 1994, 27, 107-127.

Ryan, JA; Chaney, RL. Issues of Risk Assessment and its utility in development of soil standards: the 503 methodology as an example. In: Prost R, editor. Contaminated Soils: Proc. *Third International Symposium on Biogeochemistry of Trace Elements,* Paris, May 15-19, 1995, Colloque No. 85. Paris, France: INRA Editions; 1997; 393-414.

Salanitro, JP; Dorn, PB; Huesemann, MH; Moore, KO; Rhodes, IA; Jackson, LMR; Vipond, TE; Western, MM; Wisniewski, HL. Crude oil hydrocarbon bioremediation and soil ecotoxicity assessment. *Environmental Science and Technology,* 1997, 31, 1769-1776.

Salminen, J; Haimi, J. Effects of pentachlorophenol on soil organisms and decomposition in forest soil. *Journal of Applied Ecology,* 1997, 34, 101-110.

Selivanovskaya, SY; Latypova, VZ. The use of bioassays for evaluating the toxicity of sewage sludge and sewage sludge-amended soil. *Journal of Soils and Sediments,* 2003, 3, 85-92

Sheppard, SC. Toxicity testing using microcosms. In: Tarradellas J, Bitton G, Rosell D, editors. *Soil Ecotoxicology.* Boca Raton, FL, USA: Lewis Publishers, 1997; 345-373.

Smith, EP; Cairns, J Jr. Extrapolation methods for setting ecological standards for water quality: Statistical and ecological concerns. *Ecotoxicology,* 1993, 2, 203-219.

Song, J; Zhao, F-J; McGrath, SP; Luo, Y-M. Influence of soil properties and aging on arsenic phytotoxicity. *Environmental Toxicology and Chemistry,* 2006, 25, 1663-1670.

Sprague, JB; Ramsay, BA. Lethal levels of mixed copper-zinc solutions for juvenile salmon. *Journal of the Fisheries Research Board of Canada, 1965,* 22, 425-432.

SSC-European Commission. *Harmonisation of the ecological risk assessment of chemicals.* Scientific Steering Committee. Final draft for consultation, 2003.

Stephenson, GL; Kuperman, RG; Linder, GL; Visser, S. Toxicity tests for assessing contaminated soils and ground water. In: Sunahara GI, Renoux AY, Thellen C, Gaudet CL, Pilon, A, editors. *Environmental Analysis of Contaminated Sites.* New York, USA: John Wiley and Sons. Ltd; 2002; 25-43.

Struijs, J; van de Meent, D; Peijnenburg, WJGM; van den Hoop, MAGT; Crommentuijn, Tl. Added risk approach to derive maximum permissible concentrations for heavy metals: *How to take natural background levels into account Ecotoxicology Environmental Safety,* 1997, 37, 112-118.

Suter, GW; Efroymson, RA; Sample, BE; Jones, DS. *Ecological Risk Assessment for Contaminated Soils.* Boca Raton, FL, USA: Lewis Publishers; 2000.

Tarazona, JV; Vega, MM. Hazard and risk assessment of chemicals for terrestrial ecosystems. *Toxicology,* 2002, 181-182, 187-191.

Tarazona, JV; Hund, K; Jager, T; Salonen, MS; Soares, AMVM; Skaare, JU; Vighi, M. Standardizing chemical risk assessment, at last. *Nature,* 2002, 415: 14.

Tarazona, JV; Fernández, MD; Vega, MM. Regulation of contaminated soils in Spain. A new legal instrument. *Journal of Soils and Sediments,* 2005, 5, 121-124.

Thakali, S; Allen, HE; Di Toro, DM; Ponizovsky, AA, Rooney, C P, Zhao, F-J, McGrath, S P. A Terrestrial Biotic Ligand Model. 1. Development and application to Cu and Ni toxicities to barley root elongation in soils. *Environmental Science and Technology,* 2006a, 40, 7085-7093

Thakali, S; Allen, HE; Di Toro, DM; Ponizovsky, AA; Roonev, CP; Zhao, F-J; McGrath, SP; Criel, P; Van Eeckhout, H; Janssen, CR; Oorts, K; Smolders, E. Terrestrial biotic ligand model. 2. Application to Ni and Cu toxicities to plants, invertebrates, and microbes in soil *Environmental Science and Technology,* 2006b, 40, 7094-7100.

The Ministry of Housing, Spatial Planning and the Environment. Environmental quality standards in the Netherlands (1999). *A review of environmental quality standards and their policy framework on the Netherlands.* Netherlands: Kluwer, Alpenaan den Rijn; 2001, 627 pp.

Tørsløv, J; Samsøe-Petersen, L; Rasmussen, JO; Kristensen, P. Use of waste products in agriculture. *Environmental project 366.* Copenhagen, Denmark: Danish Environmental Protection Agency; 1997.

Torstensson, L. Guidelines. Soil biological variables in environmental hazard assessment. Report No 4262. Stockholm, Sweden: *Swedish Environmental Protection Agency;* 1993

USEPA (US Environmental Protection Agency). Ecological Effects Test Guidelines OPPTS 850.2450 Terrestrial (Soil-Core) Microcosm Test. EPA 712-C-96-143. Washington, DC, USA: *US Environmental Protection Agency;* 1996

USEPA (US Environmental Protection Agency). Guidelines for Ecological Risk Assessment. EPA/630/R095/002F. Washington, DC, USA: *US Environmental Protection Agency, Risk Assessment Forum;* 1998.

Van Brummelen, TC; Van Gestel, CAM; Verweij, RA. Long-term toxicity of five polycyclic aromatic hydrocarbons for the terrestrial isopods Oniscus asellus and Porcellio scaber. *Environmental Toxicology and Chemistry,* 1996, 15, 1199-1210.

Van de Plassche, EJ; de Bruijn, JHM; Stephenson, RR; Marshall, SJ; Feitjel, TCJ; Belanger, SE. Predicted no-effect concentration and risk characterization of four surfactants: linear alkyl benzene sulfonate, alcohol ethoxilates, alcohol ethoxylated sulfates and soap. *Environmental Toxicology and Chemistry,* 1999; 18, 2653-2663.

Van Gestel, CAM; van der Waarde, JJ; Derksen, JGM; van der Hoek, EE; Veul, MEX; Bouwens, S; Rusch, B; Kronenburg, R; Stokman, GNM. The use of acute and chronic bioassays to determine the ecological risk and bioremediation efficiency of oil-polluted soils. *Environmental Toxicology and Chemistry,* 2001, 20, 1438-1449.

Van Gestel, CAM; Henzen, L; Dirven-Van Breemen, EM; Kamerman, JW. Influence of soil remediation techiques on the bioavailability of heavy metals. In: Sunahara GI, Renoux AY, Thellen C, Gaudet CL, Pilon A, editors. *Environmental Analysis of Contaminated Sites.* New York, USA: John Wiley and Sons. Ltd; 2002; 361-388.

Van Straalen, NM; Denneman, CAJ. Ecotoxicological evaluation of soil quality criteria. *Ecotoxicology and Environmental Safety,* 1989, 18, 241-251.

Van Straalen, NM; Van Gestel, CAM. Soil invertebrates and micro-organisms. In: Calow P, editor. *Handbook of Ecotoxicology,* Vol 1. 1st Ed. Oxford: Blackwell Scientific Publications; 1993; 251-277.

Vegter J, Lowe, J, Kasamas H. *Sustainable management of contaminated land: an overview.* Austria: Umweltbundesamt GmbH; 2003.

Wagner, C; Løkke, H. Estimation of ecotoxicological protection levels from NOEC toxicity data. *Water Research,* 1991, 25, 1237-1242.

Weyers, A; Sokull-Klüttgen, B; Knacker, T; Martin, S; Van Gestel, CAM. Use of Terrestrial Model Ecosystem data in environmental risk assessment for industrial chemicals, biocides and plant protection products in the EU. *Ecotoxicology,* 2004, 13,163-176.

# INDEX

Index